MATTER AND ANTIMATTER

MATTER
AND
ANTIMATTER

MAURICE DUQUESNE

*Director of Research in Nuclear Physics
at the Radium Institute, Paris*

SCIENCE TODAY SERIES

HARPER & BROTHERS
Publishers   *New York*

HARPER & BROTHERS

49 East 33rd Street, New York 16, N.Y., USA

Translated by
A. J. POMERANS
from *Matière et Antimatière*
first published in France

CONTENTS

PLATES

INTRODUCTION

The reader might wonder why a work setting out to discuss the latest developments in nuclear physics should be called *Matter and Antimatter*. The reason is that the recent discovery of anti-protons and anti-neutrons, completing the list of antiparticles, has led physicists to coin the word 'antimatter'. We shall be careful in our use of this word, if only to bring it down from the fantastic heights to which the popular press has elevated it.

On the whole, attempts at popularisation are laudable enough, but when it comes to modern physics they are fraught with danger. Here reality is often represented by mathematical equations beyond the reader's grasp, a fact which encourages many a sensationalist writer to indulge in fantasies.

The current interest in anti-particles is by no means due to their novelty—their existence was predicted in a theoretical paper published as long ago as March 1930, and the first anti-particle (the positive electron) was observed and identified in 1933. At the time the news caused no stir outside the very narrow circle of specialists.

Nowadays, the moment a new particle is identified, it is announced to the public, and despite the reserve of physicists, the popular press has no hesitation in pontificating about its unknown properties.

Though not brand-new, therefore, the problem of anti-particles is nevertheless of great interest, not only because of the old questions it resolves but also because of the new questions it poses.

The discovery of anti-protons and anti-neutrons has confirmed the general validity of the theory, presented by Dirac, a young English mathematician, to the Royal Society on the 6th December, 1929.

Do anti-particles have the property of combining to form a negative anti-nucleus which, together with positive electrons would make up an anti-atom? Is this how we must conceive the structure of so-called antimatter?

Inasmuch as so small a book can do justice to the labours of some of the greatest scientists of the past thirty years, I shall try to show what discoveries have led physicists to ask these and similar questions.

1

Atomic Theories

Up to the time when the atom bomb fell on Hiroshima, the public had heard little about the atom or its nucleus, though physicists had long suspected that it contained gigantic reserves of energy. Overnight, the atom, which had previously not even been thought worthy of inclusion in the school physics syllabus, had reached the headlines of the daily press.

Since then, we have had more than enough occasion to hear of it: atom bombs, hydrogen bombs, cobalt bombs, atomic piles, atomic generators, and the use of radio-elements in medicine and biology. During the last ten years a whole host of new discoveries and technological applications have made the term 'atom' a household word.

Even so, before we can understand the nature of the atom, we must have an idea of the structure of matter in general. A brief historical sketch of the evolution of atomic theories will allow us not only to distinguish between them but also to stress the chief characteristics of modern physics.

New ideas often lead to confusion, to an impasse or even to contradictions. Science has to mark time until some hypothesis produces a clarification, i.e. until it resolves the contradiction by means of precise definitions, no matter if these run counter to current thought, common sense or even apparently to reason.

In this way new concepts often make their appearance as mere 'words' without any concrete significance. In the 19th century when the wave nature of light was first demonstrated, science seemed to have reached a dead end. Waves are propagated in elastic media vibrating under the action of a force. Thus air vibrates and propagates sound—air is the elastic medium which carries the sound. Sound cannot be propagated in a vacuum. Yet it is a vacuum which fills interplanetary and interstellar space through which light travels with a velocity of 300,000 km per second. How could a vacuum provide the elastic medium required for the propagation of light waves? A new contradiction had made an already obscure situation even more confused.

A mere 'word' led to a breaking of the deadlock: the existence of 'ether', which served as the necessary elastic medium, was postulated. Light was simply a vibration of the ether. And the ether? . . . Well, it was no good insisting on too strict a definition of its properties—they were imponderable.

And for a time the ether did in fact serve its purpose. But if mere words could be left to resolve scientific problems, physics would very soon turn into metaphysics. A word must explain, and in explaining it must be integrated into the body of knowledge to whose wider understanding it has contributed. The word must be made to represent a geometrical or mechanical image. It is in this way that mathematics enters into physics.

The 'image' or model is an aid to scientific thought, and for a time it takes the place of physical reality. But only for a time, since science cannot rest on its laurels, even when it has discovered a complete and self-consistent explanation. The day comes when a new experiment has to be interpreted. If the model proves inadequate to this task, it has to be modified. Further experiments may lead to further modification until eventually the whole model may have to be scrapped.

Sometimes a geometrical model becomes corroded by a type of abstract formalism, and ends up as a set of mathematical formulae which explains and predicts nothing but itself.

'Words', 'models', 'mathematical formulae'— atomic theory has gone through all these stages, and this is true of every constituent element of the atom, the nucleus no less than the electron.

The Greeks introduced the notions of the void and the discontinuity of matter in order to solve what they thought were the contradictions between sensory experience and Being. Being—real existence —was by definition eternal, immutable and static. To explain such real phenomena as change and motion, Leucippus and his pupil Democritus split up 'Being' into atoms moving through a void. Like 'Being' itself, atoms were eternal and immutable, but gave a better picture of external reality.

'We say sweet, we say bitter, we say hot, we say cold, we say coloured—but in fact nothing exists beyond atoms and the void'. (Democritus).

At first, the 'atom' was nothing but a 'word' connoting certain abstract properties, the properties of 'Being'. But hardly a century had passed before the Greeks made attempts to depict it. A desire to understand the properties of matter, drove them to investigate its form and motion.

The first to give a geometric description of the atom was Epicurus, and Lucretius went into greater detail still. However, the Greeks were concerned with the surface of the atom alone. The problem of the internal structure of these ultimate particles of matter was not posed. The surface alone was thought to account for all the known phenomena.

It was not until the 17th century, that the part which mathematics could play in physics was more fully recognised.

'No one can read the great book of the universe who ignores its language, the language of mathematics', said Galileo.

The Law of Gravitation had enabled Newton to explain Kepler's Laws of Planetary Motion; the same Law ought equally to hold for atoms. Mathematics had begun to pierce the atomic surface, formerly the sole seat of all atomic properties, but experimental science was unprepared for this task. We shall see what powerful means were eventually needed for penetrating into the interior of the atom. Newton's age lacked these means, and atomic theory, though freed from the naive surface picture, was long to remain bogged down in abstraction.

In the next century a new start was made. Experimental chemists, under the indirect influence of the atomic theory of Democritus, showed that the chemical laws of combination seemed to point to discontinuities in matter. Thus, after twenty centuries, the atomic structure of matter was given an experimental basis. But in being rediscovered the atom had once again become a 'word'.

'If I had my way I should erase the word "atom" from the vocabulary of science, convinced as I am that it transcends experiment, and that in chemistry we must never transcend experiment'. (Dumas.)

During the 19th century, atoms and determinism were the undisputed masters of science. The 'proportional numbers' of the elements were calculated, and the properties of gases explained, by assuming gases to consist of perfectly elastic particles. Although the order of magnitude of the atomic radius (10^{-8} cm) was known, no attempt was made to construct a new model. Something was missing, and atomic theory was marking time.

In the course of the 20th century, the atom, indestructible according to Democritus, solid according to Newton, indivisible by definition, began to fall apart in the hands of physicists, who had by then found a new means of studying it, viz. the passing of electric currents through gases. The ensuing decomposition of the atom led to advances in atomic theory, since the newly discovered constituent parts led to the reconstruction of a model of the atom, thus providing an explanation of the properties of matter.

Since gases are not perfect insulators, a current passing through them behaves in much the same way as it does in passing through an electrolyte. The reader will recall that the number of atoms liberated during electrolysis is proportional to the quantity of electricity passing through the solution.

In about 1880, this result led physicists to postulate an elementary electric charge. This charge was even named—it was called the electron.

The study of the passage of a current through a gas inside a tube is simplified by the fact that the gaseous particles are not in contact with one another, and that no other forces than those resulting from atomic collisions need be considered.

At very low pressures (of the order of 10^{-5} mm of mercury), rays can be seen emanating from the cathode of the tube to produce a fluorescent spot on the opposite wall of the tube. The study of these cathode rays (and particularly their deflection by magnetic and electric fields) led scientists to conclude that the rays were made up of negatively charged high-velocity particles, i.e. the electron had been discovered experimentally.

This particle of electricity was characterised by two magnitudes: its electric charge e and its mass m. The passage of a current through the electrolyte was then explained as follows:

In solution, the molecules of a compound are dissociated into two ions—one charged with negative and the other with positive electricity. Thus sodium chloride ($NaCl$) in aqueous solution splits up into two ions, Cl^- and Na^+. The electric field between the electrodes leads to a displacement of the charges, the Na^+ ion travelling towards the cathode and the Cl^- ion towards the anode.

The passage of a current through a gas at weak pressure can be explained by supposing that, in the very strong electric field between the electrodes, certain ions of the gas are accelerated by the electric field, thus becoming projectiles which can break up the other, neutral, atoms. The electrons which constitute the cathode rays are the products of this destruction. They are accelerated in a sense opposite to the remaining parts of the atoms, the positive ions, which form the so-called canal rays.

Since electrons could be split off from all the elements, they were clearly constituent parts of atoms; the problem of the atomic structure had been posed anew.

J. J. Thomson thought that the electrons were embedded in a homogeneous and indivisible sphere of positive electricity, in such a way that each electron was held in a state of equilibrium due to the attractive force of the positive charge on the one hand, and the repulsive force of the electrons on the other.

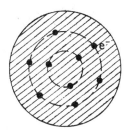

Fig. 1

J. J. Thomson's model of the atom. The negative electrons are enclosed in a sphere of positive electricity.

This model (see Fig. 1) was used in an attempt to explain the following known properties of matter:

1. The emission of visible light by bodies raised to a high temperature.

2. The emission of X-rays of the same nature as, but of very much smaller wave length than, visible light, whenever cathode rays strike against an obstacle.

3. The emission by heavy atoms of α, β and γ radiation: i.e. natural radioactivity discovered by Pierre and Marie Curie.

α-rays, somewhat similar to, but much faster than, canal rays, were identified as twice-ionised helium atoms.

β-rays, though much faster than cathode rays were found to consist, like the latter, of negative electrons.

γ-rays were found to be similar to X-rays but much more penetrating.

J. J. Thomson explained the atomic emission of light and X-rays by assuming the electrons to be in a state of vibration.

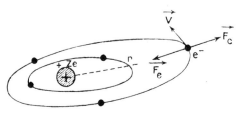

Fig. 2

Jean Perrin's model of the atom. The electrons revolve about the central positive charge.

In this model, the vibrations of the internal rings of electrons would account for the emission of X-rays and those of the external (positive) rings for the emission of visible light. A different model was suggested by Jean Perrin (see Fig. 2), who assumed that each atom was a miniature solar system in which, at relatively immense distances, the electrons revolved about a 'sun' of positive electricity, and on orbits along which the electric force and the force of inertia were in equilibrium.

After Rutherford's experiments on the scattering of α-particles in passing through a metallic screen, Jean Perrin's model was adopted and improved, while that of J. J. Thomson had to be discarded. The fact that a projectile can cross a barrier made up of many thousands of atoms without being deflected by them, makes it clear that the atoms cannot be the 'solid' structures J. J. Thomson imagined them to be. On the other hand, a 'planetary atom' with its empty spaces could easily explain the experimental results.

The new picture of the atom looked as follows:

A positive charge at the centre contains almost the entire mass—this is the nucleus. On the basis of Rutherford's experiments its radius was calculated to be of the order of 10^{-13} cm. Recalling that the radius of the atom is of the order of 10^{-8} cm we see that the nucleus, representing the entire positive charge of the atom, is 100,000 times smaller than the latter. The large space surrounding the nucleus contains negative charges, i.e. the planetary electrons which revolve about the nucleus with varying velocities, and whose number is such as to render the atom electrically neutral.

However, when physicists tried to use this new model to explain other phenomena, they encountered new difficulties and a host of contradictions.

Highly complicated calculations and extremely delicate experiments were needed before the arrangement of the electron shells was understood well enough to account for all the experimental results. In the course of this work, which, inter alia, was to lead to the notion of anti-particles, there was born a new physics whose assumptions removed the contradictions besetting its path.

To make any progress, scientists at the beginning of the 20th century had to submit all the basic concepts of science to a strict and critical re-examination. They had to revise scientific principles and methods. They were forced in particular to re-examine their notions of time and space and to question the continuous nature of energy—the result was relativity and quantum theories. Probability began to force its way irresistibly into the new physics, and gave rise to wave mechanics.

We shall give a rapid sketch of these new theories and show how they enabled physicists to resolve the difficulties with which they were faced at the dawn of the 20th century.

2

Relativity

Referring to the theory of Relativity, Emil Borel once remarked: 'Einstein has not only given us a physical theory, he has provided us with a new way of looking at the world'.

An attempt to convey to the public a theory that has upset our most familiar concepts—those of space and time—is not likely to be a rewarding task. Acquaintance with this theory is, however, essential if one is to understand the subject-matter of this book: the significance of anti-particles.

The better to appreciate the originality of Einstein's contribution, we shall first outline the classical mechanics of Galileo and Newton.

In its study of motion (kinematics), mechanics introduces two quantities, space and time. In the old mechanics these two quantities were independent of each other.

We cannot observe a body M moving in space without a suitable reference system. Every such reference system has an origin O and three perpendicular axes Ox, Oy and Oz.

The position in space of the moving body M is defined by three co-ordinates x, y and z, which are functions of the time t. M is thus characterised by four magnitudes, three of space and one of time.

In three-dimensional physical space, the moving body M describes a trajectory which can be represented geometrically.

Geometry treats of the properties of space and of the possible constructions in it. We shall now define some of the elements which make these geometrical constructions possible.

For Euclidean geometry the essential element is a straight line, which is given certain *a priori* properties.

Euclidean geometry assumes that through a given point there can be only one straight line parallel to a given straight line.

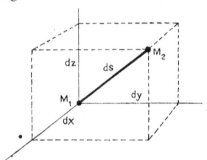

Fig. 3
Definition of Euclidean space.

$$M_1 \ (x_1, y_1, z_1)$$
$$M_2 \ (x_1 + dx, y_1 + dy, z_1 + dz)$$
$$M_1 M_2 = ds$$
$$ds^2 = dx^2 + dy^2 + dz^2$$

For ordinary purposes, the properties of space are adequately described by the simplified picture of Euclidean geometry, and time can be considered to be independent of space (see Fig. 3). In other words, time can be represented by a magnitude t which is independent of the three magnitudes x, y, z.

Having adopted definitions of space and time, we must now choose a reference system in which the laws of mechanics apply.

Two such systems are possible:

1. *The Copernican System of Co-ordinates*—The origin is the centre of gravity of the solar system. The three axes Ox, Oy, Oz are determined in space by the fixed stars.

2. *The Galilean System of Co-ordinates*—A system of co-ordinates which is in rectilinear translatory motion with respect to the Copernican system of co-ordinates (i.e. moving with a constant velocity).

In three dimensional Euclidean space, two points M_1 and M_2, infinitesimally close, and defined by the co-ordinates:

$$M_1 \begin{cases} x_1 \\ y_1 \\ z_1 \end{cases} \qquad M_2 \begin{cases} x_2 = x_1 + dx \\ y_2 = y_1 + dy \\ z_2 = z_1 + dz \end{cases}$$

(where dx, dy, dz are infinitely small increments of the co-ordinates x, y, z), are separated by a distance $M_1 M_2 = ds$.

By the theorem of Pythagoras, ds is given by the equation:

$$ds^2 = dx^2 + dy^2 + dz^2$$

This expression characterises Euclidean space, in which the definition of ds^2 does not involve time or physical magnitudes.

How can we pass from one Galilean system to another Galilean system? In other words, once we have stated that a point M(x', y', z', t') in a reference system O′ moves with uniform velocity $\vec{v}$ with respect to another reference system O, how can we define the point M (x, y, z, t) in O with respect to O′?

To simplify the problem, let us suppose that O′ moves with respect to O along the Ox axis (Fig. 4) and that when t = O, O′ coincides with O.

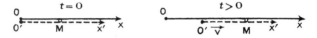

Fig. 4

Classical rule for the composition of velocities.

OM = OO′ + O′M; $x = vt + x'$

Clearly the only co-ordinates affected by the motion are those along the direction of the displacement. We then obtain the following system of equations, known as the Galilean transformation:

$$x' = x - vt$$
$$y' = y$$
$$z' = z$$
$$t' = t$$

This system of equations allows us to pass from M(x, y, z, t), the co-ordinates of M with respect to O,

to   M(x', y', z', t'), the co-ordinates of M with respect to O′.

It follows from these equations that the distance between two fixed points is the same, i.e. invariant, no matter whether their co-ordinates are referred to the system O or to the system O′.

In other words, the Galilean transformation leaves distances invariant.

Nor does the transformation alter the form of the fundamental equation of Newtonian dynamics $\vec{F} = m\vec{\gamma}$, where $\vec{\gamma}$ is the acceleration of a body of mass m acted upon by a force $\vec{F}$.

The fact that the equations of classical mechanics remain invariant under the Galilean transformation, leads to the conclusion that no mechanical experiment can ever demonstrate the motion of a system O′ with respect to a system O.

Now, while the equations of classical mechanics remain invariant under the Galilean transformation, Maxwell's electro-magnetic equations do not. If this is true, properly designed experiments involving electro-magnetic phenomena such as the propagation of light, should show a displacement of the earth with respect to the ether. Such an experiment was made by Michelson and Morley, but the result was negative.

The theory of relativity was born out of this difference between the mechanical and electro-magnetic equations or, from an experimental point of view, out of the negative result of the Michelson and Morley experiment.

Light, according to Fresnel, was a vibration of the ether, i.e. the 'elastic medium' supporting the light waves and which filled the cosmos. Once Maxwell had shown that light could be explained as being propagation of an electro-magnetic field, the importance of the ether diminished. The ether simply became the 'medium in which Maxwell's equations hold'.

In its annual orbit about the sun, the earth moves with a velocity of about 30 km/s. with respect to the ether. If the ether were immobile, the observer's motion with respect to it ought to be demonstrable. The Michelson-Morlay experiment had precisely this aim in view.

Let us fix in the ether a co-ordinate system Ox, and on the earth a co-ordinate system $O'x'$ in uniform rectilinear motion with velocity $\vec{v}$ with respect to Ox. A source of light in O emits a light wave which is propagated along Ox with velocity $\vec{c}$. This wave is represented by the displacement with velocity $\vec{c}$ of a point M in Ox.

Let us measure the time taken by this wave to travel a distance $AB = l$ in $O'x'$.

1st case: $v = O$. O' does not move with respect to O.

To travel the distance AB, light takes the time

$$t_1 = \frac{l}{c}.$$

2nd case: $v > O$. O' is displaced in the positive sense of Ox.

The relative velocity of M in the system O' is $c - v$, and the time taken to travel the distance AB is

$$t_2 = \frac{l}{c - v}.$$

3rd case: $v < O$. O' is displaced in the negative sense of Ox.

The relative velocity of M in the system O' is $c + v$, and the time taken to travel the distance AB is

$$t_3 = \frac{l}{c + v}.$$

In short, we ought to observe that $t_2 > t_3$ and that $t_2 > t_1 > t_3$.

The experiment was negative; the classical rule for adding velocities had broken down. The velocity of light was found to be constant and independent of the motion of the source with respect to the observer. (Velocity, it will be recalled is a ratio resulting from the division of space by time.)

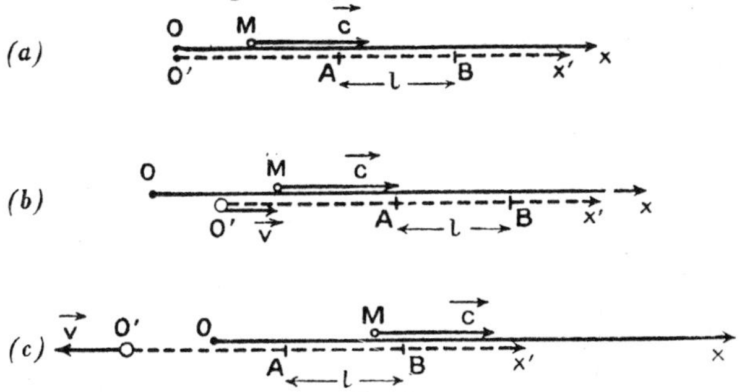

Fig. 5

Since the time remained constant, Lorentz, in order to account for the Michelson-Morlay experiment assumed that moving bodies or systems contract in the direction of their motion. Lorentz set up a new system of equations, known as the Lorentz transformation, to replace the Galilean transformation. Using the same notation as before:

$$x' = \frac{x - vt}{\sqrt{1 - \dfrac{v^2}{c^2}}}$$

$$y' = y$$
$$z' = z$$

$$t' = \frac{t - \dfrac{vx}{c^2}}{\sqrt{1 - \dfrac{v^2}{c^2}}}$$

If v/c is small, i.e. if the velocity of O' with respect to O is small compared with that of light, the equation is reduced to Galileo's formula, and in particular we obtain $t' = t$. Furthermore, it is found that Maxwell's equations remain invariant under the Lorentz transformation.

In 1905, after having submitted the classical notions of absolute time and space to a trenchant examination, Einstein proposed an elegant explanation of the Lorentz transformation.

He enunciated the following two principles:

1. The laws of physical phenomena, and particularly the laws of electro-magnetism are the same in all Galilean reference systems.

2. For all Galilean reference systems the velocity of light is the same in all directions.

The first principle meant that it was the Lorentz transformation and not the Galilean transformation which was physically significant. In other words no experiment in magnetism, *as well* as in mechanics, made within a Galilean system could ever lead to a demonstration of its motion with respect to another Galilean system.

The second principle involved a modification of the law of the addition of velocities.

In classical mechanics, if v is the velocity of O' with respect to O, u' and u the velocities of a point M in O' and O, the theorem of the addition of velocities is expressed as:

$$u = u' + v$$

In Einstein's mechanics, this theorem becomes:

$$u = \frac{u' + v}{1 + \frac{u'v}{c^2}}$$

If v/c is small we recover the classical law:

$$u = u' + v$$

In the preceding examples, where the velocity of M, a source of light in O, is equal to c ($u = c$), classical mechanics leads to $u' = c + v$, while Einstein's mechanics leads to $u' = c$, irrespective of v, — a result in perfect agreement with experiment.

We stated earlier that the element ds^2, defined by

$$ds^2 = dx^2 + dy^2 + dz^2$$

characteristic of Euclidian space, had the same value in all Galilean systems. The Lorentz equations, in introducing a transformation of the time t associated with an event E at the point M (x, y, z), changes the form of the element ds^2. We must now consider the representation of an event in four-dimensional space (x, y, z, t), known as the Minkowski four-dimensional space.

If we consider the displacement of an electromagnetic wave between two infinitesimally close events E_1 (x_1, y_1, z_1, t_1) and E_2 (x_2, y_2, z_2, t_2), and if we designate this element of space by $d\sigma$, we obtain $d\sigma^2 = dx^2 + dy^2 + dz^2$ (Fig. 6). If dt is the time taken by the wave to cross the space $d\sigma$, and if, as we have seen, the velocity of light is constant

$\left(\frac{d\sigma^2}{dt^2} = c^2 \right)$, we obtain:

$$ds^2 = c^2 dt^2 - d\sigma^2 = 0$$

Thus the expression $ds^2 = c^2dt^2 - dx^2 - dy^2 - dz^2$ has the same value in all Galilean systems, and like the ds^2 of Euclidean space remains constant in all ordinary three-dimensional space. ds is the 'world line' and if two events E_1 and E_2 correspond to a velocity lower than c $ds^2 > O$, this interval becomes O for velocities equal to that of light; i.e. $ds^2 = O$.

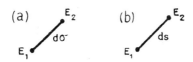

Fig. 6
(a) Ordinary space $d\sigma^2 = dx^2 + dy^2 + dz^2$
(b) Space-time $ds^2 = c^2dt^2 - dx^2 - dy^2 - dz^2$

The negative result of the Michelson-Morley experiment together with the Lorentz transformation which accounts for this negative result demanded a modification of our ideas about the structure of space.

Other modifications were equally imperative. It was necessary that the equations of dynamics, just like those of electro-magnetism should also remain invariant under the Lorentz transformation. However, the equations of Newtonian dynamics which remain invariant under the Galilean transformation, do not remain invariant under the Lorentz transformation. Thus Newtonian dynamics had to be modified.

Designating by $\vec{p} = m\vec{v}$, the momentum of a point of mass m and of velocity $\vec{v}$, the fundamental equation of classical dynamics

$$\vec{F} = m\vec{\gamma}$$

becomes

$$\vec{F} = \frac{d\vec{p}}{dt}$$

In relativity dynamics, the momentum $\vec{p}$ is expressed by $\vec{p} = \dfrac{m_0\vec{v}}{\sqrt{1 - \dfrac{v^2}{c^2}}}$, which is consistent with

$(\vec{p} = m\vec{v})$ so long as we make $m = \dfrac{m_0}{\sqrt{1 - \dfrac{v^2}{c^2}}}$, (where

m_0 is the inertial mass of the material point, and m its relativistic mass).

It will be seen that m increases with v. In classical dynamics, a material point, not acted upon by any force, describes rectilinear uniform motion with respect to the Galilean axes. In the new dynamics it describes a curved 'world line' for which $ds_2 > O$ in Minkowski's four-dimensional space. Though Minkowski's space is no longer Euclidian, straight lines and planes nevertheless play a paramount role in it. In this four-dimensional space, light has a rectilinear 'world line' with $ds_2 = O$. Amongst these trajectories or 'world' lines there are some with a privileged direction corresponding to $ds_2 > O$, which runs from the past to the future.

In classical mechanics, the energy of a particle of mass m and of velocity v was given by its kinetic energy:

$$E = \tfrac{1}{2} mv^2$$

In relativity mechanics the energy of a particle is given by the expression

$$E = mc^2; \qquad E = \frac{m_0 c^2}{\sqrt{1 - \dfrac{v^2}{c^2}}}$$

or else by $\qquad E^2 = c^2 (p^2 + m_0^2 c^2).$

When the velocity of the particle is zero ($v = O$), its energy is greater than zero, and its value $m_0 c^2$ represents a new magnitude in physics: the energy of the particle at rest. In the course of developing a dynamics which would remain invariant under the Lorentz transformation, physicists had thus become aware of the close correlation between mass and energy. This correlation had been ignored by classical physics. Einstein shook the modern world by introducing matter as an inexhaustible store of energy.

The restricted theory of relativity introduced many other fruitful ideas into physics. We shall discuss these at greater length when we come to Dirac's notion of material particles with negative energy. For the time being we shall merely note that in Einstein's equation

$$E^2 = c^2 (p^2 + m_0^2 c^2),$$

E can have a positive or negative value, i.e.

$$E = \pm\, c \sqrt{p^2 + m_0^2 c^2}$$

Similarly, if ds is positive and $dt > O$ in the equation $ds^2 = c^2 dt^2 - d\sigma^2$, which allows us to put the relativity mass

$$m = m_0 \frac{dt}{\left(\dfrac{ds}{c}\right)}$$

m will be positive, and the energy $E = mc^2$ will also be positive.

But there is no mathematical reason why we should not make ds negative and, with $dt > 0$, this always gives a negative value for the mass, and thus for the energy E.

At first this problem did not concern physicists unduly, but in about 1930 the success of quantum theory and the development of wave mechanics forced them to look more closely into the matter. The consequent experimental work led to the discovery of anti-particles.

In emphasising the interdependence of space and time, the restricted theory of relativity focussed attention on the structure of space about which Euclidian geometry had made certain a priori assumptions.

In 1916, when Einstein was endeavouring to generalise relativity theory in such a way that the laws of motion, including those produced by gravitational forces, could be expressed in the simple form of the restricted theory of relativity, he was forced to use a more highly generalised geometry than that of Euclid.

Riemann had rejected the idea that space was independent of the phenomena that took place in it, and had therefore formulated a much more general element ds^2, i.e.:

$$ds^2 = \sum_{i,k} G_{ik}\, dx_i\, dx_k$$

$$x = x_1,\, y = x_2,\, z = x_3,\, ct = x_4$$

The Euclidian element ds^2 could only represent an empty universe, and the element ds^2 of Minkowski's four-dimensional space held only for the restricted theory of relativity. By introducing Riemann's element ds^2, Einstein effected a synthesis between geometry and physics. He showed, in effect, that the determination of the coefficients G_{ik} depends on the distribution of masses in the universe. This new four-dimensional space assumes neither straight lines nor planes—it is curved and the geodetic lines of the element ds^2 define the notion of the masses and the propagation of light.

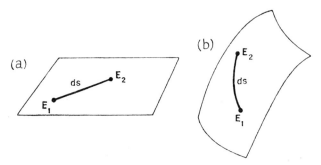

Fig. 7
(a) Euclidean space-time.   (b) Riemann space-time.

Newton had explained the appearance of gravitational forces by means of the law of universal gravitation:

$$F = k\,\frac{mm'}{r^2}$$

The track of an anti-proton, —P, produced by the Bevatron at the University of California and recorded in a liquid-propane bubble chamber. The anti-proton is annihilated on striking a proton in a carbon nucleus, producing a 'star' of pi-mesons. The short track at C is the surviving fragment of the nucleus.

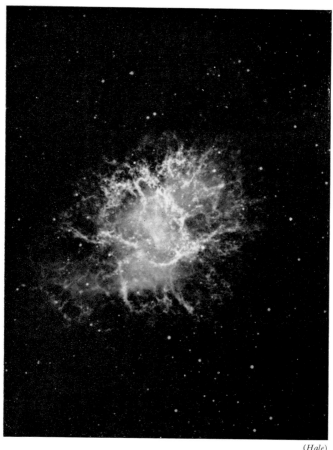

(*Hale*)

The Crab Nebula in Taurus is 4,000 light-years distant
and is a member of our own Galaxy. It consists of the
expanding gases of a star which exploded as a supernova
in A.D. 1054, and is a powerful radio-transmitter with a
strong magnetic field. Its radio output of 10^{24} kilowatts
is consistent with the presence of antimatter.

In the general theory of relativity, gravitational forces result from the use of curvilinear co-ordinates in a space that is curved by the presence of matter within it.

We shall conclude with some remarks on the limits of classical mechanics and Euclidian geometry.

For ordinary purposes, the world is contained between limits represented by the terrestrial radius of 6,370 km, or $6 \cdot 37.10^8$ cm on the one hand, and by the dimensions of bacteria, i.e. $0 \cdot 1\mu$ or 10^{-5} cm on the other hand. Within these limits, Euclidian geometry and classical mechanics are in agreement with experiment and thus play a useful role.

But man has carried his experiments well beyond these limits into the realm of the atom and into that of the stars. Now, the radius of the atomic nucleus is 10^{-13} cm, and the distance separating us from the nearest star is $3 \cdot 10^{18}$ cm. The proven everyday tools were found wanting when it came to these dimensions. Other tools had to be forged, of which the old ones were a very good approximation on our normal scale.

Einstein's mechanics and Riemann's geometry were the new tools which allowed man to extend his knowledge well beyond the limits within which he had previously been held prisoner.

3

Quantum Theory

Despite the inroads it had made into classical ideas of space, time, mass and energy, Einstein's mechanics had done nothing to shake the notion of the continuity of physical magnitudes. It was left to Planck, in the course of constructing a physics on the atomic scale, to introduce discontinuous variations of physical magnitudes.

Quantum theory was born out of the need to interpret experiments on black body radiation.

A 'black body' is one whose inner walls emit and absorb radiation depending solely on the temperature of the body and not on its shape or nature.

In their attempts to predict the distribution of black body radiation for a given temperature, scientists found that new hypotheses had to be made. It was discovered that the total radiation per unit surface is proportional to the fourth power of the absolute temperature of the black body—this is the Stefan-Boltzmann law ($W = kT^4$).

If we consider the energy due to radiations whose wave lengths lie between λ and $\lambda + d\lambda$ to be $E \; d\lambda$ per second per unit area, then the total energy emitted per second per unit area is given by:

$$W = \int_0^\infty E_\lambda \; d\lambda$$

This, by Stefan's Law, is equal to $k\mathrm{T}^4$.

Now, for a given temperature T, E_λ can be experimentally determined for every wave length λ, and a graph of E_λ against λ can be plottted (Fig. 8).

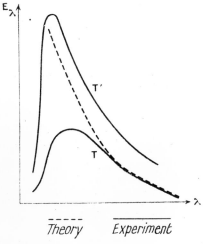

Fig. 8
Black-body radiation.

The area under each curve represents the sum $\int_0^\infty \mathrm{E}_\lambda \, d\lambda$, i.e. the total emissive power at that temperature. A theoretical interpretation of this experimental curve had now to be given.

This interpretation was based on the following model (Fig. 9): the walls of the body are assumed to contain systems of charged particles (electrons, atoms, molecules) which oscillate with varying frequencies about an equilibrium position. Now whenever an electrical charge becomes displaced inside the wall, an electro-magnetic wave is emitted, and conversely, whenever an electro-magnetic incident wave strikes the wall, the charged system is set into vibration.

From this model a *theoretical* curve of E_λ against λ can be calculated (Rayleigh's law).

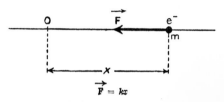

Fig. 9

Model of an oscillator. The simplest type of oscillator is made up of a charged particle of charge e and of mass m whose acceleration along its path is directed towards a fixed point in that path, and varies as its distance from this fixed point. The motion of the charge is then defined by $x = A \sin \omega t$.

This is shown as a dotted curve in Fig. 8, from which it can be seen that the curve tends towards infinity at small values of λ and that, consequently, the integral $\int_0^\infty E \, d\lambda$ becomes infinite also.

The classical treatment of the oscillator model thus led not only to disagreement with experiment, but to the absurd result that the total emissive power was infinite.

Planck, while holding fast to the oscillator hypothesis, and to the laws governing the motions of the oscillating particles, restricted the possible number of oscillations, and thus managed to make the theory agree with the experimental findings. In particular, he made restrictions applying to high frequency radiation (small wave lengths) and, in 1900, he put forward the supplementary hypothesis that an oscillator of frequency v could only emit or absorb radiant energy by finite quantities (quanta) equal to hv.

Such discontinuous emission of energy tends to play down high frequency radiation. The greater the frequency, the more energy is needed by the oscillator to emit radiation—high frequency radiation has thus a smaller probability of emission.

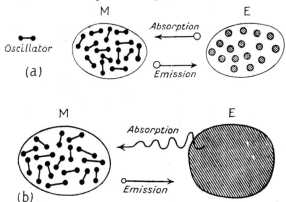

Fig. 10
Energy exchanges between matter and radiation.   M, matter.   E, energy.

Just like in the case of matter and electricity, the discontinuous character of energy was revealed. Though the particles of energy, or quanta, differ in magnitude, all are defined by the equation $E = hv$ (h = Planck's constant = $6 \cdot 55.10^{-27}$ in the C.G.S. system.

On the basis of this hypothesis, the new theory could take one of two forms:

1. All energy exchanges between matter and radiation (absorption and emission) take place by quanta. Radiation itself is discontinuous (Fig. 10 (a)).

2. Absorption is continuous and there is a continuous accumulation of radiant energy, while emission takes place by quanta (Fig. 10 (b)).

Since the wave theory of light had a strong experimental basis, the second interpretation, which implied that radiation was of a continuous nature, seemed to be the more probable.

But, in 1887, Hertz had already discovered a phenomenon, which was difficult to fit in with the wave theory of light.

Hertz had discovered that matter, when submitted to the action of radiation, emits electrons spontaneously. If we designate the radiation by its intensity I and its frequency v, and the ejected electrons by their number N and their energy $E = \frac{1}{2} mv^2$, we arrive at the following results:

(*a*) E varies with the frequency v alone and not with the intensity I;

(*b*) N varies with the intensity I.

Energy is needed to tear the electron from matter; this energy can only be derived from the incident radiation—matter absorbs energy. If the absorption is continuous (hypothesis 2), the energy taken up by the electron is proportional to the intensity of the incident wave, and this energy, evenly distributed along all the points of the wave, varies inversely with the square of the distance between the point under consideration and the source of light. According to this hypothesis, then, the energy E of the electrons should have been independent of the frequency ν of the radiation and furthermore, if the source is at a great distance, the intensity of the incident wave cannot be great enough to tear out any electrons (Fig. 11 (a)). In fact, experiments did not bear out this conclusion.

In 1905, Einstein formulated hypothesis No. 1, namely that matter absorbs radiation discontinuously, and that radiation itself has a corpuscular structure, the radiant energy transmitted being proportional to the frequency of radiation in such a way that

$$E = h\nu.$$

The corpuscle of energy was called the photon. A return to the corpuscular structure of light had been effected, and, in particular, Hertz's discovery (the so-called photo-electric effect) could now be explained.

In the new hypothesis, the energy is located at a point in the incident beam and does not fall off according to the inverse square law (Fig. 11 (b)). When a photon with energy $h\nu$ strikes an object, its energy may be great enough to tear out an electron and to impart kinetic energy to it.

If E is the energy needed for extracting an electron, then its kinetic energy W is given by

$$W = h\nu - E$$

It will be seen that W is a function of only the frequency ν of the incident radiation.

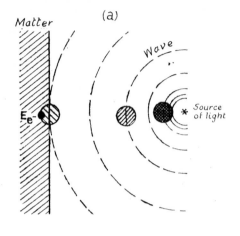

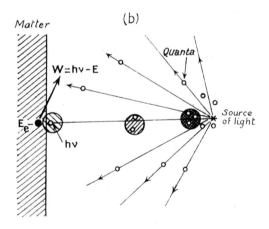

Fig. 11

The interpretation of the photo-electric effect (a) Wave theory. The electron does not receive sufficient energy to be torn out. (b) Theory of photons. The electron receives sufficient energy to be torn out.

The intensity I of the radiation can be represented by the number of photons per unit volume. Since these photons travel in all directions, their number diminishes with increase of distance from the source in such a way that, on the average, the inverse square law is recovered.

In these circumstances, one would normally expect the number of ejected electrons to be related to the number of photons per unit volume, i.e. to the intensity.

In our discussion of the photo-electric effect, it emerged that radiation was made up of corpuscles of energy, i.e. of light quanta or photons. However, when attempts were made to construct a model of this new particle, new difficulties arose. The fact that frequency played an integral part in the definition of this new particle ($E = h\nu$), showed that wave theory still governed the behaviour of corpuscles in such a way as to thwart all attempts at constructing a model. It was left to wave mechanics to effect a reconciliation between the corpuscular and wave theories.

We shall return to this problem later, but we must first discuss other models of the atom investigated by relativity and quantum theories.

4

The Bohr-Sommerfeld Atom
and the New Physics

We have seen how J. J. Thomson's and Jean
Perrin's atomic model became the basis for attempts
to explain the then known properties of atoms and
particularly their emission of light and X-rays.

While Michelson and Morley's experiment forced
physicists to revise their notions of absolute time
and space, and while the experimental study of
black-body radiation gave rise to the first physical
theory, viz. quantum theory, experimental techniques to probe the atom were making unprece-
dented headway. Scientists were busy with the study
and classification of the spectrum of radiation
emitted by atoms under the action of thermal or
electric excitations, or under electron bombardment.

Early 20th century atomic physicists were tackling
a similar task to that tackled earlier by the chemists
who, following in Dalton's footsteps, had classified
the elements according to their relative weights.
We know that this arduous work had led these
chemists to the demonstration of the periodic nature
of the elements.

Physicists, in their turn, by effecting a classification
of atomic radiations, were trying to bring some order
into the complex spectral phenomena, the better to

formulate the empirical laws on which atomic models could be constructed.

It soon emerged that a simple equation with only one variable (a single parameter) could describe all the visible lines of the hydrogen spectrum. As more experimental evidence became available, physicists concluded generally that *every frequency found in the spectral line of an atom could be expressed as the difference between two term numbers (T_1 and T_2) characteristic of the energy levels of that atom.*

The physical reality behind these term numbers had now to be investigated.

Could the planetary model based on Rutherford's experiments, explain the existence of such discontinuous energy states? In that model, the planetary electron described a Keplerian orbit about the positive central nucleus and, according to classical electro-magnetic theory, it was therefore bound to radiate energy. As a consequence, its kinetic energy decreased, and the electron was drawn in towards the nucleus. There was nothing discontinuous at all about this process. Tempting though it was, the model of the planetary electron ran counter to the laws of electro-magnetism and to the stability of matter.

We have seen how a search for the physical reality behind the so-called 'spectral terms' had become imperative. As early as 1913, quantum theory had stood the test of experiment, and just as Planck had quantized radiation, so Bohr now quantized the atom.

In doing so, he had to make far-reaching assumptions that would solve the contradictions. Holding to the planetary model, and, for the sake of simplicity, considering only Keplerian circular orbits with a single parameter, Bohr made the following assumptions:

1. The atom exists only in certain stationary states (orbits) with certain selected energy values E_n, in which the integer n is called the principal quantum number.

2. In these stationary states, the atoms do not emit photons.

3. The atoms emit energy (radiation) only when they jump from one stationary state (orbit) n to another stationary state n'.

Riemann, by rejecting Euclid's axiom, had founded a new geometry on the cosmic scale; by quantifying Jean Perrin's planetary model and ignoring the laws of electro-magnetism, Bohr had created a new physics on the atomic scale.

In Quantum Theory, the circular motion of a mass m revolving with angular velocity ω on an orbit of radius a, is given by:

$$ma^2\omega = \frac{nh}{2\pi} \quad \text{where } \omega = \frac{nh}{2\pi} \cdot \frac{1}{ma^2} \qquad (1)$$

For each value of the radius a there exists a corresponding series of values of ω, such that $n = 1, 2, 3$, etc.

Apart from these assumptions, Bohr preserved the laws of classical mechanics: in a stationary orbit (on which it does not emit energy even though subject to strong acceleration), the electron revolving with velocity $\vec{v}$ is held in equilibrium by the electro-

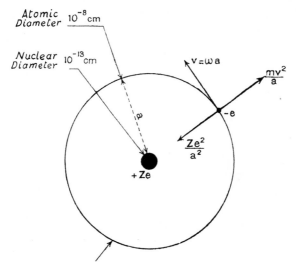

Fig. 12
Bohr's model of the atom.

static attraction $\dfrac{Ze^2}{a^2}$ between the positively charged nucleus

Ze and the force of inertia $\dfrac{mv^2}{a}$.

$$v = \omega a, \quad \text{whence} \quad \frac{Ze^2}{a^2} = m\omega^2\, a \qquad (2)$$

Eliminating ω between (1) and (2) we obtain:

$$a = \frac{n^2\, h^2}{4\,\pi^2\, mZe^2} = \frac{n^2}{Z} \cdot 0 \cdot 528.10^{-8}\ \text{cm}.$$

The kinetic energy of the electron is $E_c = \frac{1}{2} ma^2\omega^2$, and its total energy $E = E_c + E_p$, E_p being the potential energy. The energy in the nth orbit is:

$$E_n = \frac{-2\,\pi^2\,mZ^2\,e^4}{n^2\,h^2}$$

The equation shows that the energy is proportional to Z^2/n^2, and thus inversely proportional to n, i.e. it decreases with distance from the nucleus.

In this model the position of the electron is determined by the parameter n:

$$n = 1 \quad \textit{level } K \quad \textit{ionisation energy } E_K$$
$$n = 2 \quad \text{,, } L \quad \text{,,} \quad \text{,, } E_L$$
$$n = 3 \quad \text{,, } M \quad \text{,,} \quad \text{,, } E_M$$

In his model Bohr ignored the structure of the atomic nucleus, but the emission of α-radiation by naturally radio-active elements makes it probable that it consists of hydrogen or helium nuclei.

Bohr's simple model explains a great number of experimental data on the nature of optical spectra and of X-rays.

During absorption, a photon of energy $E = h\nu$ penetrates into the atom; this energy may be used for wresting an electron from the hold of the positive nucleus. It may then jump from the level L to the level M by absorbing the energy $E_L - E_M$. If the energy is great enough, the electron (in level L, for instance) can be ejected altogether, with kinetic energy $W = h\nu - E_L$. This explains the photo-electric effect discussed earlier.

During emission the converse happens. An electron (in level L, for instance), may drop to a vacant place in level K and emit a photon of energy $h\nu = E - E_L$.

If the transition takes place between deep levels, the energy $h\nu$ of the emitted photon is large and X-rays which have high frequency, are emitted;

if the transition takes place between outer levels, where the force of attraction of the nucleus is weakest, the radiation is correspondingly weak, and radiation in the ultra-violet and visible spectrum is emitted.

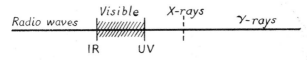

Fig. 13
The spectrum of electro-magnetic waves.

Clearly Bohr's model is very attractive—so much so that we are almost tempted to forget that accepting it means rejecting the classical theory of electro-magnetism.

Still, the model is incomplete, since only circular orbits have been considered. Experiments were soon to emphasise this drawback.

Improvements in the techniques of detecting and recording atomic emission lines made it obvious that certain lines classified as simple were, in fact, of a complex nature.

To account for this fact, theoreticians had to modify and elaborate Bohr's model to cover elliptical orbits and also nuclear motions within the atom.

This work was started by Sommerfeld in 1916. Quantizing elliptical orbits, he used relativity mechanics to explain the motion of electrons in them. The energy of the electron became characterised by two quantum numbers, n and l, the latter taking all integral values between O and $n - 1$.

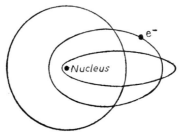

Fig. 14
Sommerfeld's model of the atom.

$$E_{n,\,l} = E_n\left\{1 + \frac{\alpha^2 Z^2}{n^2}\left(\frac{n}{l+1} - \frac{3}{4}\right)\right\}$$

Where E_n is the Bohr energy, and α the so-called fine structure constant (E is a function of the two parameters n and l).

While Bohr's model provided one K-level, one L-level and one M-level for the spectral terms of X-rays, Sommerfeld's model gave one K-level, two L-levels and three M-levels.

Bohr	*Sommerfeld*
$n = 1 \quad E_K$	$n = 1 \quad l = 0 \quad E_K$
$n = 2 \quad E_L$	$n = 2 \begin{cases} l = 0 & E_{L0} \\ l = 1 & E_{L1} \end{cases}$
$n = 3 \quad E_M$	$n = 3 \begin{cases} l = 0 & E_{M0} \\ l = 1 & E_{M1} \\ l = 2 & E_{M2} \end{cases}$

The new theory agreed more closely with experiment. Research was making great headway, and it was soon discovered that the L-level had a fine structure of 3 and not of 2 lines, and the M-level of 5 instead of 3.

In order to elaborate his theory, Sommerfeld introduced the supplementary quantum number *j*, whose meaning remained obscure. This complication of the theory bode ill for the Bohr-Sommerfeld model. The effect on atomic radiation by a magnetic field was to deliver a final blow to that model.

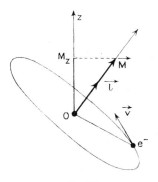

Fig. 15

The orbital angular momentum and its projection on the axis OZ.

The doubling of spectral lines under the action of a magnetic field had been predicted as early as 1896, and Zeeman had been the first to observe it.

To explain the so-called 'Zeeman effect', we must first define some of the terms used to describe it.

The *orbital angular momentum* of the electron is the momentum of the electron in its orbit about the nucleus. It acts in a direction perpendicular to the plane defined by the momentum $\vec{p} = m\vec{v}$ and the atomic nucleus taken as the origin O (see Fig. 15).

In wave mechanics the orbital angular momentum $\vec{M}$ is quantized i.e. $\vec{M}$ is made to correspond with a vector $\vec{l}$ which has $2l + 1$ discrete orientations in space.

$\vec{M}$ and $\vec{l}$ are related by the equation $\vec{M} = \dfrac{h}{2\pi}\, \vec{l}$.

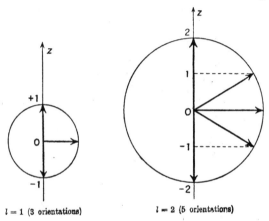

$l = 1$ (3 orientations) $l = 2$ (5 orientations)

Fig. 16

Quantizations of the orbital angular momentum $\vec{M}$.

The quantum number l is proportional to the angular momentum $\vec{M}$.

The directions of $\vec{l}$ are referred to a fixed axis OZ which has no physical significance. (Fig. 16). M_z represents the projection of the momentum $\vec{M}$ on this axis; like $\vec{M}$, M_z is quantized.

Thus $l = 1$ leads to three possible directions of the angular momentum $\vec{M}$, and $l = 2$ to five directions, though both levels are characterised by the same energy $E_{n,l}$ which is a function of only the quantum n and l. This point is important, for we shall soon see that if the atom is situated in a magnetic field, the three states ($l = 1$) and the five states ($l = 2$) will have different energies with a consequent separation of levels (Zeeman effect).

Magnetic moment. The revolutions of the electrons about the nucleus set up electric currents which transform the atom into a small magnet of magnetic moment $\mathcal{M}$. For an electron which describes a circular orbit of radius a with velocity $\vec{v}$ the magnetic moment $\mathcal{M}$ is given by:

$$\mathcal{M} = \frac{e}{2c} av$$

Since the orbital angular momentum of such an electron is $\vec{M} = ma\vec{v}$ the magnetic moment $\mathcal{M}$ is clearly related to the orbital angular momentum $\vec{M}$ in such a way that:

$$\mathcal{M} = \frac{e}{2mc}\vec{M} \quad \text{and} \quad \mathcal{M}_z = \frac{e}{2mc}M_z$$

In the magnetic field $\vec{\mathcal{H}}$, the electron will have the additional energy

$$\Delta E = \mathcal{M}_z \mathcal{H} = \frac{e}{2mc}M_z \mathcal{H}$$

The effect of a magnetic field on the spectral lines is an extremely complex phenomenon, and the interpretation of experimental results extremely difficult.

The theory could only account for a part of this effect (the normal Zeeman effect), while another effect, i.e. the anomalous Zeeman effect remained unexplained. The fine structure of the spectra proved much more complex than the theory had indicated.

For instance, if an atom in the state $l = 1$ is placed in a magnetic field $\vec{\mathcal{H}}$, it has three different energy levels corresponding to the three values of M_z, i.e. $+ 1, 0, - 1$ (Fig. 16).

In a magnetic field, the energy level corresponding to $l = 1$ is split into three levels, and that of $l = 2$ into five levels. This is the normal Zeeman effect (Fig. 17).

$$\text{——} \ E_{n,\,1} \cdot + \frac{e}{2\,mc} \frac{h}{2\,\pi} \ \mathcal{H}$$

$$\text{——} \ E_{n,\,1} \cdot \qquad\qquad \text{——} \ E_{n,\,1}$$

$$\text{——} \ E_{n,\,1} \cdot - \frac{e}{2\,mc} \frac{h}{2\,\pi} \ \mathcal{H}$$

$$\mathcal{H} \neq 0 \qquad\qquad \mathcal{H} = 0$$

Fig. 17

In this theory, already burdened with the quantum number j, three parameters served to define the state of the electron: n, l, j. Even so, they proved inadequate, and in 1925, there was a return to an earlier model in which the electron was likened to a sphere with evenly distributed negative charge $(- e)$. By Einstein's formula, $E = mc^2$, the radius of this sphere was calculated to be $2 \cdot 8.10^{-13}$ cm. This was the order of magnitude of nuclear dimensions.

To explain the anomalous Zeeman effect, the picture had to be modified by the introduction of an additional parameter. The electron was imagined to spin on its own axis like a top, thus having an intrinsic angular momentum, the so-called 'spin'. Just like the angular orbital momentum, spin, too, became quantized:

$$\vec{M}_{rot} = \frac{h}{2\pi}\vec{s}$$

The value of s was chosen as half the quantal unit $\frac{h}{2\pi}$ so as to agree with experiment: $s = \frac{1}{2}\frac{h}{2\pi}$.

The spin of the electron implied the existence of an intrinsic magnetic moment:

$$\vec{\mu} = \frac{e}{2mc}\vec{M}_{rot} \qquad \mu_z = \frac{e}{2mc}M_{z\ rot}.$$

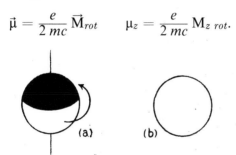

Fig. 18 .
Electron (a) with spin. (b) without spin.

The electron could be likened to a small spherical magnet rotating about its own axis (Fig. 18). By experiment, its magnetic moment was shown to be:

$$\mu = \frac{e}{2mc}\frac{h}{2\pi}.$$

With the introduction of spin the difficulties were resolved, and Sommerfeld's quantum number j

assumed a new significance as the vector sum of the orbital and spin angular momenta: $j = l + s$. The anomalous Zeeman effect could now be explained.

Did science at last have a true picture of the atom? A certain number of rules were still needed to complete it, and to account for all the experiments.

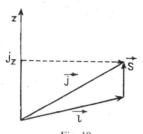

Fig. 19
Total angular momentum $\vec{j}$.

If, for instance, we imagine a system of two electrons (1) and (2), we can arrange them in four ways: two with parallel spin and two with anti-parallel spin.

Each electron has the magnetic moment μ, and if their spins are parallel (Fig. 20a), their magnetic moments reinforce each other, while with anti-parallel spin (Fig. 20b) the resultant magnetic moment is zero.

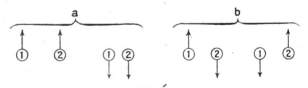

Fig. 20
Different arrangements of spin for a system of two electrons.

Such a system does in fact exist: the helium atom with its two electrons in the K-shell ($n = 1$). The absence of a magnetic moment would indicate that the two electrons have anti-parallel spin; in the stationary state two electrons in the K-shell seem to be precluded from having parallel spin. We may generalise this result by stating that an electron is characterised by the quantum numbers n, l, j and by the quantum number j_z, the projection of j on the axis OZ (Fig. 19). The Pauli exclusion principle states that no two electrons in the same atom may have four quantum numbers of the same value.

This exclusion principle limits the number of possible combinations *a priori*—for instance it restricts the number of electrons on the K-level to 2. For the L-level ($n = 2$) we have two electrons when $l = O$ and a maximum of six electrons when $l = 1$.

The cloud of electrons round the nucleus had given way to a geometrical picture involving no more than four parameters and a number of combination rules. The model fitted the experimental facts, but even so physics was soon to outgrow it. Physics was fast becoming too abstract for any models of atoms or electrons, and Louis de Broglie and Heisenberg with their wave and matrix mechanics were soon to throw an entirely new light on the whole problem of the structure of matter. The new wave mechanics was at first non-relativistic (Schrödinger). When Dirac introduced relativity into the new wave mechanics, and when he presented his paper to the Royal Society, the idea of anti-particles was born, and with it science was given its first glimpses of the possible structure of antimatter.

5

Wave Mechanics and Indeterminism

In the Bohr-Sommerfeld atom, quantum considerations had been superposed on classical mechanics, but no real synthesis had been effected.

Relativity mechanics was concerned with the mechanics of continuous physical magnitudes. Quanta, which played such a predominant role in physical phenomena, now called for an entirely new mechanics.

This new mechanics (wave mechanics) took över from quantum mechanics the notion that radiation is discontinuous, and inferred that the electron itself must have undulatory properties.

According to an hypothesis put forward by Louis de Broglie in 1925, the quantization of the stationary orbits in the Bohr-Sommerfeld atom reflected one aspect of this undulatory nature:

'Whenever a material element in the most general sense possible, has an energy W in any reference system, there occurs in this system a periodic phenomenon with the frequency v defined by the quantum relation $W = hv$'. (Louis de Broglie).

In classical mechanics the momentum of a material particle is defined by the relation

$$\vec{p} = m\vec{v}$$

In relativity mechanics this expression became

$$\vec{p} = \frac{m_0 \, \vec{v}}{\sqrt{1 - \dfrac{v^2}{c^2}}}$$

Now, in wave mechanics a wave length λ was made to correspond with the momentum $\vec{p}$ of the electron; Planck's constant, which had been instrumental in introducing the idea of the corpuscular nature of radiation, now served to introduce the undular nature of material particles, in such a way that the wave length of the associated wave was

given by $\lambda = \dfrac{h}{p}$

Experimental confirmation of this revolutionary hypothesis was not long in coming.

In 1927, Davisson and Germer in America, and later G. P. Thomson in England, showed that whenever an electron beam passed through an extremely thin metal foil, diffraction phenomena comparable to those obtained with X-rays, could be observed. In passing through the foil, the electrons were deflected not like particles but like waves with a frequency roughly a million times that of visible light.

'As a result of his experiments, (G. P.) Thomson came to the conclusion that each electron is associated with a wave whose wavelength is approximately h/mv, the length of the train being at least 50 wavelengths and the breadth of the wave front at least 30×10^{-8} cm. When the electron is moving with uniform velocity and is in a steady state, if there is any energy in the train of waves it must travel with the velocity of the electron, which is small compared with that of light'. (J. J. Thomson, *Recollections and Reflections*, London 1936, p. 348).

Physicists had long wondered about the nature of the wave associated with an electron. From 1923 to 1927, Louis de Broglie had tried to 'obtain a clear and coherent picture of the wave-corpuscle dualism in the framework of space and time' that conformed to classical, causal, ideas.

At the same time other physicists, and particularly Heisenberg, had dropped the idea of a picture in favour of an interpretation based on probability— hence the name 'probability wave' which is some- times used to designate the wave associated with an electron.

This new interpretation became generally accepted.

In 1926, Schrödinger, starting from classical mechanics, gave a complete analytical development of a wave mechanics that bore the same relationship to classical mechanics as physical optics bore to geometrical optics.

Wave mechanics, perhaps even more so than the theory of relativity, revolutionised our way of thinking. While relativity and quanta had forced physicists to revise their notions of space, time and energy, wave mechanics questioned the causality of classical mechanics.

In this new mechanics, each particle is character- ised by a wave function ψ. The function ψ can be resolved into the sum of functions of the mono- chromatic waves of frequencies $v_1, v_2, v_3, \ldots$ and of amplitudes $a_1, a_2, a_3 \ldots$, i.e.

$$\psi = a_1 \psi_1 + a_2 \psi_2 + a_3 \psi_3 + \cdots$$

In classical physics, the intensity of a wave is given by the square of its amplitude; in wave mechanics the square of the amplitude of a particular component, e.g. a_2, gives the probability that the particle will have the energy $E_2 = h\nu_2$.

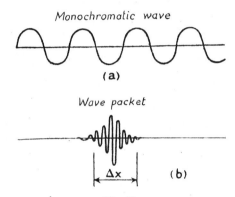

Fig. 21

Description of a particle in wave mechanics. (a) When the energy is strictly defined ($\Delta E = 0$), the position is not ($\Delta x = \infty$). (b) When the energy is not strictly defined ($\Delta E \neq 0$), the position is somewhat more precisely defined ($\Delta x \neq 0$).

A monochromatic wave has a definite frequency and wave length λ, and hence the energy of the corresponding particle is definite; its uncertainty ΔE is zero. On the other hand the electron cannot be localised in space since the wave itself occupies the whole of an extended region of space—here the uncertainty $\Delta x = \infty$ (Fig. 21a).

If instead of a monochromatic wave, we take a train of waves whose wave lengths vary between $\lambda_0 + \Delta\lambda$ and $\lambda_0 - \Delta\lambda$, the particle can be located with greater accuracy and Δx may become very small, while the uncertainty in the value of the energy expression is increased by the fact that the frequency is no longer strictly defined ($\Delta E \neq 0$) (Fig. 21b).

The uncertainty relation between the co-ordinate x of a particle and its velocity v is defined by:

$\Delta x \cdot \Delta v = \dfrac{h}{2\,\pi\,m}$, where m is the mass of the particle. Clearly, if m is very great (which happens when we leave the atomic for the human scale), $\dfrac{h}{m} \simeq 0$, and the uncertainty disappears.

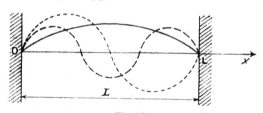

Fig. 22
Electron in an enclosure.

This uncertainty in the values defining the position and the velocity of a particle, is characteristic of the transition from classical mechanics to wave mechanics.

Let us now consider an electron oscillating between two reflecting walls (Fig. 22). From the point of view of wave mechanics we have a system of stationary waves

$$\psi = A \sin \frac{2\,\pi\,x}{\lambda}.$$

At the walls, i.e. for $x = O$ and $x = L$, ψ must be equal to zero, and therefore

$$\frac{2\pi}{\lambda} L = n\pi$$

where n is an integral number.

The possible wave lengths are then $\lambda_1 = 2L$ $(n = 1)$,

$$\lambda_2 = \frac{2L}{2}\ (n = 2),\quad \lambda_3 = \frac{2L}{3}\ (n = 3)\ldots\quad \lambda_n = \frac{2L}{n}.$$

A given energy can be assigned to each value of λ. From the relations:

$$E = \tfrac{1}{2} mv^2 \quad \text{and} \quad p = \frac{h}{\lambda} \quad \text{or} \quad p = mv$$

we obtain:

$$E = \tfrac{1}{2} m \left(\frac{h}{m\lambda}\right)^2 \quad \text{or} \quad \lambda = \frac{2L}{n}$$

and finally:

$$E_n = \tfrac{1}{2} m \frac{h^2\, n^2}{m^2\, 4\, L^2} = \frac{n^2\, h^2}{8\, mL^2}.$$

This set of possible values for the energy, results from the boundary conditions at the walls, which require that

$$\frac{2L}{\lambda} = n\pi.$$

If we now consider an electron in an atom, and in an orbit of length $2\pi a$, which is a multiple of the wave length associated with the electron, we will have a system of stationary waves, just as in the previous example of the electron in an enclosure.

From such a system of stationary waves we obtain a discontinuous series of values for the energy, but we cannot simultaneously define the position of the electron in the system. Only the probability of its presence in a given orbit can be predicted.

The phase of the wave seems to have a definite physical significance since it allows us to define the energy of the corpuscle. On the other hand, since the amplitude is uniformly distributed in a monochromatic wave, the precise position of the particle becomes indeterminate, thus eluding all attempts at a physical localization.

Since determinism demands the localization of a particle of given energy, wave mechanics and the uncertainty principle can be said to have introduced indeterminism into physics.

At present, a great deal of research is being done in order to lead wave mechanics along the paths indicated by de Broglie in 1927. At that time, De Broglie put forward his 'theory of the double solution' which admitted the existence, behind the statistical wave of wave mechanics, of a wave of singularity.

Whatever happens in this respect, the new wave mechanics were able to account for most of the experimental results arising from work on the Bohr-Sommerfeld atom, with the notable exception of the anomalous Zeeman effect, which, as we have seen, was resolved by the introduction of the notion of electron spin.

Schrödinger's non-relativistic equation had not taken this important factor into account, and was therefore not applicable to systems of particles whose velocities were not neglible when compared with that of light.

Dirac, in deriving a relativistic expression for the equations of electron waves, was able to show that the notion of spin was automatically included in his new formulation.

In the course of his generalisation which introduced relativity theory into wave mechanics, he revolutionised the mathematical representation of the properties of matter.

6

Dirac's Theory

Schrödinger's wave mechanics did not take into account the spin of the electron. His wave equation defined the function ψ as a scalar quantity, i.e. a quantity which is completely specified by its magnitude, as distinct from a vector quantity which also needs its direction to be stated.

To introduce spin into wave mechanics, Pauli proposed a wave function ψ having two components corresponding to the two possible orientations of the spin. Though the new wave function represented an advance on Schrödinger's theory, it was still based on classical mechanics.

In Schrödinger's equation the wave function associated with the electron was related to the energy W of the electron. In classical mechanics, the energy W of a particle is a function of its velocity $\vec{v}$ or of its momentum $\vec{p}$, i.e.:

$$W = \tfrac{1}{2} mv^2 = \frac{1}{2m} p^2$$

which always gives a positive value for W. In relativistic mechanics these equations become:

$$W^2 = m_0^2 c^4 + c^2 p^2$$

Cygnus-A, at a distance of 270 million light-years, is one of the most powerful known radio-transmitters and appears to be a pair of colliding galaxies. Its observed radio output of about 10^{33} kilowatts can be calculated on the assumption that it contains some antimatter.

(*Mt. Wilson and Palomar*)

The globular galaxy M 87, in Virgo, appears to be either ejecting or absorbing a bright blue jet of matter. It emits intensely powerful radio and light waves that can be accounted for if it is assumed that the galaxy has encountered a patch of antimatter which is now undergoing annihilation.

whence

$$W = \pm\, c\sqrt{m_0^2\, c^2 + p^2}$$

which gives W either a positive or a negative value.

This point is very important for the theory of anti-particles, and this is why, despite the difficulties involved, we have tried to tell the reader something about the theory of relativity.

In giving a relativistic form to Schrödinger's equation, Dirac showed that the wave function ψ is a magnitude with four components and that the new equations are invariant under the Lorentz transformation. The reader will appreciate that, as a consequence, the new wave mechanics satisfies the special theory of relativity. Nor was this its only advantage: Dirac's equations in which the spin and the magnetic moment of the electron were implicit—relativity had introduced them there—was able to account for all the experimental evidence, including the anomalous Zeeman effect.

It turns out that, since the velocity of the electron is small with respect to that of light, two components of Dirac's wave function can be neglected, and we are left with the two components of Pauli's theory.

It is beyond the scope of this book to give Dirac's famous equations which solved so many problems. Suffice it to say, that in 1928 physics had reached such heights of abstraction that the idea that a model was always necessary had to be renounced altogether.

On the 6th December, 1929, in his paper on the theory of electrons and protons, Dirac stressed an inherent difficulty in his theory—relativity had introduced into it the possibility of electron energies which were negative.

In the relativistic form of W, where $m_0 c^2$ represents the energy of the electron at rest, the electron cannot take values between $- m_0 c^2$ and $+ m_0 c^2$. W is positive when $m_0 c^2 > 0$, and negative when $m_0 c^2 < 0$ (see Fig. 23).

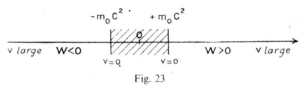

Fig. 23

Both in classical and in relativity theory W could be stipulated to be positive, since, because energy had to vary continuously, there was no way of jumping the gap between $+ m_0 c^2$ and $- m_0 c^2$.

In quantum theory, on the other hand (and wave mechanics is, of course, a quantal mechanics), energy may vary discontinuously and thus jump the barrier $2m_0 c^2$ to pass from W > 0 to W < 0, and vice versa.

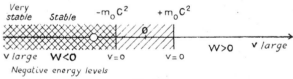

Fig. 24

Hence there is no reason in wave mechanics for precluding solutions with negative energy.

If this new idea was not to be rejected outright, a

physical meaning had to be given to these solutions, and this Dirac tried to supply. Though an electron with negative energy was quite foreign to our experience, Dirac argued that it could nevertheless be studied theoretically, and in particular its behaviour in any given electro-magnetic field could be predicted. The result of the calculation both in classical mechanics and in quantum theory, was that an electron of negative energy is deflected in a magnetic field exactly like an electron of positive energy would be if it had a positive electric charge $+ e$.

In his paper of December 1929 Dirac wrote, 'Thus an electron with negative energy moves in an external field as though it carries a positive charge. This result has led people to suspect a connection between the negative-energy electron and the proton or hydrogen nucleus'.

Dirac then goes on to point out that 'one cannot, however, simply assert that a negative-energy electron *is* a proton, as that would lead to the following paradoxes: a transition of an electron from a state of positive to one of negative energy would be interpreted as a transition of an electron into a proton, which would violate the law of conservation of electric charge . . . A negative-energy electron will have less energy the faster it moves and will have to absorb energy in order to be brought to rest. No particles of this nature have ever been observed'. [*Proc. Roy. Soc.* A.*126*, 360-5 (1929-30)].

The Theory of 'Holes'. Negative energy could only be explained by further revolutionary hypotheses. This is what the young English theoretician did when, in his paper, he suggested a solution to 'the inherent difficulty of negative energy'.

Let us recall that the most stable states of a particle are those which have the lowest energy. In the case of electrons, the most stable levels, according to Dirac's theory, are those with negative energy and with a large velocity v. All electrons would tend to drop to these levels with emission of radiation. Dirac suggested the following way out of the difficulty.

By the Pauli exclusion principle, only a single electron can be found in each of these levels. Assuming that all negative energy states are occupied, except perhaps some corresponding to small velocities, electrons with positive energy would have little chance of undergoing transitions to the negative energy levels. Hence it is only electrons with positive energy which we observed in the laboratory.

On the negative energy side we have an infinity of electrons distributed over the most stable levels, and electrons with negative energy have never been observed experimentally, precisely because they are distributed over space in infinite number and because they are in the most stable states possible.

Though this hypothesis might not satisfy physicists accustomed to models, it has tremendous implications since, if there were indeed a small number of states of negative energy that were unoccupied, i.e. if lacunae occurred among the otherwise fully occupied negative energy states, then we might hope to be able to observe them.

Dirac investigated the properties of these lacunae or 'holes' in the continuous distribution of negative energy states, and showed that the motion of a 'hole' in an external electro-magnetic field is equivalent to the motion of a *positive* charge $+ e$ with *positive* energy, from which it followed that 'the holes in the distribution of electrons with positive energy are protons'.

This theory of holes explained why it was difficult to identify electrons of negative energy with protons —the transition of an electron $W > 0$ to a state $W < 0$ corresponds to the collision of an electron with a proton in which there is a simultaneous disappearance of the two particles, accompanied by the emission of radiation.

In connection with this paper of Dirac's, it is interesting to note that after having shown that the holes behave just like positively charged particles. Dirac identified these holes with the only particles of positive charge $+ e$ then known, viz. the protons.

Why did he then not postulate at once the existence of a new particle of the same mass as the electron and of charge $+ e$—the anti-electron? Dirac's conclusion seems to show that a theoretician, once he has erected a highly abstract system, feels the need to re-establish contact with experimental reality as quickly as possible. The positive charge $+ e$ having crept into his very elegant theory, Dirac immediately identified it with the proton.

But he was quick to notice the great discrepancy between the mass of the proton and that of the electron.

On the 29th May, 1931, in a second paper, Dirac stated that experimental work had made it clear that the particle corresponding to the hole must necessarily have the same mass as the electron. Quoting the work of Weyl and Oppenheimer who had suggested that the hole in the negative energy states must be considered as a new type of particle, Dirac proposed calling this particle the anti-electron. He pointed out that the difficulty of detecting the new particles was due to their strong tendency to recombine with ordinary negative electrons.

The annihilation of matter, and the materialisation of energy were thus foreseen as early as 1931, in a paper which even suggested that protons might also have their own negative states, normally occupied, except for a small number of unoccupied states which would appear as anti-protons.

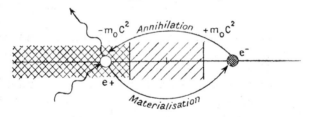

Fig. 25
Materialisation and annihilation.

Since then the theory has undergone many modifications, and become even more abstract. Even so, the sudden development of atomic energy and the associated problem of anti-particles have recently revived interest in it.

Though the theory of holes may have lost its practical interest for physicists who now work with more up-to-date mathematical tools, it has retained much of its explanatory value, since it allows us to form a concrete picture of very abstract processes.

Imagine a flat-bottomed box containing a hundred small billiard balls distributed evenly over the bottom, and so close together that in effect they form a continuous layer covering the bottom of the box. Individual balls cannot be distinguished or observed.

Now if the same box contained one hundred and fifty balls, fifty of these would not fit into the bottom layer and would lie above the others. The hundred balls covering the entire bottom of the box can be likened to electrons with negative energy $W < m_0 c^2$; the fifty others behave like ordinary negative electrons with positive energy $W > m_0 c^2$ — these alone can be observed and their movements and interactions studied.

Let us now imagine that an external force manages to extract one of the hundred balls of the bottom layer. This could be done, for instance, by a small suction pump or by striking a ball in some suitable way. The ejected ball would now leave an observable gap as it rose to the top. The ball would then represent the positive energies of the hole theory. The gap it has produced in the bottom layer (representing the negative energies) can also be observed. It can be likened to a particle of positive energy since it corresponds to the absence of a particle of negative energy, and it will have a positive charge since it corresponds to the absence of a negative charge. This 'hole' in the layer of negative electrons with negative energy will then behave like a positive electron with positive energy. Side by side with the classical electron we therefore have the possibility of the existence of an anti-electron—the positive electron or positron.

The hole will not remain empty for long, since one of the fifty-one balls on the higher level (positive energies) will tend to fall into it, thus closing the gap in the bottom layer. In the analogy, two particles will then have disappeared—the electron and the positron.

This picture may have served to illustrate the disappearance of matter which occurs when an electron and an anti-electron annihilate each other. Their total energy—including the energy $2m_0 c^2$ corresponding to their mass—must be converted into photons.

The converse phenomenon—the creation of an electron-anti-electron pair—requires an energy higher than $2m_0 c^2$. From the values of m_0 and c, the photon necessary to provide this energy can be calculated to have an energy higher than one million electron volts.

At this point, it might be useful to sum up the characteristics of the electron and of the hypothetical anti-electron.

	Electron e^-	*Anti-electron e^+*
Charge	$-1 \cdot 6.10^{-19}$ C	$+1 \cdot 6.10^{-19}$ C
Mass	$0 \cdot 91.10^{-27}$ g	$0 \cdot 91.10^{-27}$ g
Spin	$\frac{1}{2}$	$\frac{1}{2}$
Magnetic moment	$- eh/4 \pi mc$	$+ eh/4 \pi mc$

The positive electron was not to remain a hypothetical particle for long. Experiment was soon to confirm the existence of this anti-particle.

7

Experimental Physics at the Beginning of the Twentieth Century: The Positive Electron

So far, we have tried to retrace the steps taken by modern physical theory in its attempts to improve on the classical explanation of atomic phenomena. If we have devoted so much space to theory, it is because the dawn of the twentieth century was marked by an unparalleled wealth of fruitful hypotheses. Relativity, quantum theory, and wave mechanics were leading physics towards new horizons, and had opened up to mankind an unlimited source of energy: atomic power. The theoretical developments had a direct bearing on the problem of antiparticles, and, therefore, we could not avoid discussing them in some detail. But now we must leave theory for the research laboratory in which an unceasing study of the properties of matter, and particularly those of the atomic nucleus, was being made.

Little was known about the nucleus, apart from Prout's hypothesis (1815), in which the hydrogen nucleus was the constituent element of all other nuclei. Chemists believed that the number of electrons in an atom might well be equal to half the atomic weight, and they had managed to classify the elements, first in order of atomic weight, and later according to their electronic structure.

Pierre and Marie Curie's discovery of natural radio-activity led to an entirely new approach. The study of the radio-active properties of the heavy elements was to provide a great deal of important data on the structure and organisation of the nucleus.

The discovery of isotopes, i.e. atoms of the same element having different physical but identical chemical properties, had raised problems which were to occupy physicists for the next twenty years to come.

Doubtless, the most important advance in attempts to probe the nucleus was Rutherford's discovery (1919) that nitrogen could be transformed into oxygen, with the liberation of hydrogen nuclei or protons. These particles with an equal but opposite charge to that of the electron, could only have originated from the nitrogen nuclei which, under the bombardment of particles from a naturally radio-active body, broke down to liberate one of their constituents:

$$\alpha\text{-particle} + \text{nitrogen} \rightarrow \text{oxygen} + \text{proton}$$

$$\text{He}_2^4 + \text{Ni}_7^{14} \qquad \text{O}_8^{17} + \text{H}_1^1$$

In 1920, protons and electrons still appeared to be the sole constituents of matter. At that time, Rutherford's experiments were being repeated in a great many laboratories and a new chemistry was born: nuclear chemistry.

Boron, fluorine, sodium and aluminium were all bombarded with α-particles, and these experiments

were soon to lead to the discovery of a new constituent of matter, the neutron (Chadwick, 1932),
and to the discovery of a new type of radio-activity,
'artificial' radio-activity (Irène and Frédéric Joliot-
Curie, 1934).

We shall have to return to these two great discoveries later, but meanwhile we shall continue our
tour of the laboratories, and look at the techniques
for studying radio-activity.

Rays of charged particles may be studied by observing the ionisation phenomena they produce.
This can be done in three ways:

1. Measuring the intensity of radiation (electroscope).

2. Observing the trajectory of a charged particle
(Wilson cloud-chamber).

3. Counting the charged particles (scintillation
counter and Geiger-Müller counter).

1. *Measurements of the intensity of radiation
(electroscope).* The electroscope is a box containing
a very thin gold leaf attached at one end to a fixed
metal rod. If an electric charge is brought into contact with the rod, the gold leaf is deflected from the
rod (by repulsion between like charges).

When a radio-active substance is placed inside the
box, its radiation will ionise the air in the box and the
charge on the rod will leak into the ionised air.
The gold leaf will then return to its original position.

The speed with which the foil collapses is a
measure of the ionisation in the chamber.

2. *Observation of the trajectory of a charged
particle* (Wilson cloud-chamber). The Wilson cloud-
chamber is a cylinder containing air saturated with

water vapour. A piston in the chamber is moved so as to cause the air suddenly to expand to 4/3 its volume. This produces supersaturation. The charged particles ionise the air, each giving rise to thousands of ions. Each ion becomes a nucleus on which a drop of water condenses, and the droplets are visible as they reflect light from a beam sent in through the side of the chamber. The line of droplets produced by a particle in its path through the chamber can be photographed from above.

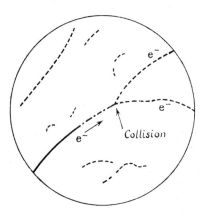

Fig. 26

Collision between a fast-moving electron and another electron (after a photograph taken in a Wilson cloud-chamber).

By placing the chamber in a magnetic field the energy and charge of a particular particle can be evaluated from the radius of its trajectory.

3. *Count of charged particles.* (*a*) Scintillation-counter. When a heavy charged particle, such as an α-particle or proton, strikes a fluorescent screen, the

resulting scintillations can be observed through a magnifying glass.

This method is no longer in use since it is both awkward and inaccurate, and we only mention it because it was due to a similar arrangement that Rutherford was able to observe the transformation of nitrogen into oxygen with the emission of a proton.

(b) Geiger-Müller counter. This is an ionisation chamber consisting essentially of an aluminium cylinder of thickness 0·1 mm. (the negative electrode) and a thin conducting wire (the positive electrode), stretched axially inside the cylinder and carefully insulated from it; this wire is kept at a potential of about 1,000 V.

When an ionised particle, i.e. a charged particle, passes through the counter, it produces ion-electron pairs (e^-; ion$^+$) which are accelerated by the electric field in the counter so that they repeatedly ionise the gas inside.

In this way, passages of the particles produce pulses in the counting wire which are led to a suitable amplifier and can be counted by a mechanical counter.

The positive electron. Round about 1930, scientists were studying α-, β- and γ-radiation and particularly their absorption by various substances. Certain anomalies during the absorption of the γ-rays emitted by thorium drew attention to work being done on cosmic rays.

Cosmic rays were discovered in 1910, when it was observed that a gold leaf electroscope is discharged at altitudes of between 5,000 and 9,000 m. This discharge showed that cosmic radiation was also made up of charged particles of great penetrative power.

In 1929, the Russian physicist Skobelzyn, studying cosmic radiation by means of the Wilson cloud-chamber, was able to show that cosmic rays had an energy of up to 15 million eV. In 1932, Anderson and Millikan, placing a Wilson cloud-chamber in a magnetic field, observed that the charged particles were being deflected. The direction and radius of their trajectory led to a determination of the sign of the charge and the mass of the particle.

From photographs of these trajectories, Anderson was led to suspect the existence of positively charged particles with a mass that was small compared to the mass of the proton. Other experiments were to confirm his findings, and the newly discovered positive particles were named positrons. When sufficient data had been accumulated, it became clear that positrons were, in fact, positive electrons, i.e. the anti-electrons of Dirac's theory. As so often happens in science, the new discovery was soon to be confirmed in other branches of physics.

We have mentioned the fact that the anomalous absorption of γ-radiation was occupying the attention of physicists during 1930-1931. What was the nature of this anomalous absorption? γ-radiation consists of photons, i.e. particles having no mass, but whose energy is still governed by the relation $E = h\nu$. Any study of γ-radiation is thus the study of the interaction between photons and matter. Now, matter is largely made up of electrons, and it is pertinent to investigate the interaction between photons and electrons. Two effects which were also being studied at that time, the photo-electric effect and the Compton effect, must first be mentioned.

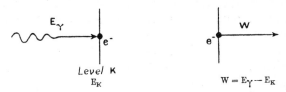

Fig. 27
Photo-electric effect.

1. *Photo-electric effect*. In this, the photon gives up all its energy to the electron, which then acquires a kinetic energy corresponding to the difference between the energy of the photon and the energy which held it in the atom from which it was ejected.

2. *Compton effect*. Here, the photon gives up only part of its energy to the electron, and continues to exist with change of frequency. As in the photo-electric effect, an electron is expelled from an atom.

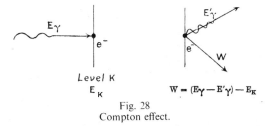

Fig. 28
Compton effect.

From the theory of these effects, physicists could predict a decrease in the intensity of a beam of γ-rays when it passed through a plate made, for instance, of lead, in such a way that:

$$\Delta I = I N \, dx \, (\sigma_{ph} + \sigma_c);$$

where   I = incident intensity;

     N = number of atoms per unit volume of the absorbing material;

    dx = thickness of the absorbing material;

   σ_{ph} = absorption by photo-electric effect;

   σ_c = absorption by Compton effect.

When incident radiation has an energy greater than 1 MeV, the absorption (or decrease in intensity ΔI is greater than the theory predicts. The explanation is as follows:

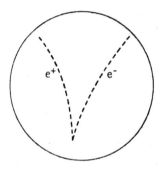

Fig. 29
Materialisation of a photon. The paths of the electrons are curved under the action of a magnetic field. The path of the photon is not visible.

By means of cloud-tracks, I. and F. Joliot-Curie managed to show that when a photon passes through a plate, it may lead to the emission of positive electrons. They obtained a photograph on which a negative and a positive electron could be seen to have originated from the same point (Fig. 29). The materialisation of energy had been demonstrated—photons with sufficient energy can disappear to create two electrons of opposite sign and charge. This explains why the absorption of high energy γ-radiation is greater than the theory predicted—

absorption due to the formation of a pair of particles (σ_p) has to be added to the expression for ΔI above. The new equation is:

$$\Delta I = IN \, dx \, (\sigma_{ph} + \sigma_c + \sigma_p)$$

Let us now look at the interpretation (within the scope of Dirac's theory) of this materialisation of energy—or, to put it more precisely, of this creation of the e^+, e^- pair.

In Fig. 30, the energy corresponding to the mass m_0 of an electron at rest is, according to Einstein's relation, $m_0 c^2 = 510$ KeV.

To create two electrons, therefore, a minimum of energy $2m_0 c^2 = 1 \cdot 02$ MeV is needed. If the energy of the photon is greater than $1 \cdot 02$ MeV, it can thus give rise to an e^+, e^- pair, the extra energy being converted into the kinetic energy of the two electrons $W_{e^+} + W_{e^-}$.

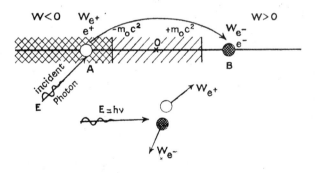

Fig. 30
The creation of an e^+, e^- pair according to the Dirac theory.

The theory of holes has shown how an electron can jump from a negative energy level A to a positive energy level B (Fig. 30). In this case a photon of energy $h\nu$ projects the negative electron across the barrier $2m_0 c^2$. In the course of this process, the photon disappears to give rise to an electron and its hole, i.e. two corpuscles.

In his theory, Dirac had also foreseen the annihilation of positive electrons by collision with negative electrons which are so abundant in matter. The lifetime of an anti-electron was thought to depend on the electron density of the absorbent material; it was believed to be of the order of 3.10^{-7} sec. in a medium such as air at atmospheric pressure. This theoretical value was of an order of magnitude in agreement with experiment; high-velocity positrons —e.g. those found in cosmic rays—could thus pass through the Wilson cloud-chamber without being annihilated.

Since its velocity decreases with successive collisions, a positive electron can become destroyed by a negative electron and give rise to two photons of total energy 510 KeV or to a single photon of energy 1·02 MeV, whenever an atomic nucleus is present to absorb the liberated momentum.

In the same year that the materialisation of energy was demonstrated, the dematerialisation of matter was also shown experimentally (I. and F. Joliot-Curie and J. Thibaud, 1933).

The energy of the photons liberated during the annihilation of an e^+, e^- pair in a lead or aluminium screen, was found to be of the order of 510 KeV, and the number of photons per positive electron was of the order of 1·6-3. This was the first experimental confirmation of Einstein's equation $E = mc^2$. *The mutual transformation of matter and energy had been proved experimentally.* To the mass m of a particle, there corresponds the energy $E = mc^2$, where c is the velocity of light.

Whenever a physical process causes the disappearance of mass, an enormous quantity of energy is liberated. A gram of matter represents an energy of $8·98.10^{20}$ ergs or $2·1.10^{13}$ cal. This energy is created each time one gram of matter is destroyed. Energy is produced whenever an anti-electron (i.e. a positive electron) is annihilated, and similarly energy will also be liberated by the destruction of any of the other anti-particles.

At the Solvay Congress, held in Brussels at the end of October, 1933, Dirac could legitimately claim that the recent discovery of the positive electron and all the experimental results so far obtained were consistent with his earlier theory about the negative energy levels of the electron.

But at the same Congress other problems were raised which must now occupy our attention, namely:

1. The discovery of a new constituent of the atomic nucleus, the neutron,
2. The interpretation of radio-activity and the neutrino hypothesis,
3. The construction of proton accelerators.

Was the neutron which, together with the proton, made up the atomic nucleus, an elementary particle obeying Dirac's equations? Were there anti-protons and anti-neutrons in addition to anti-electrons?

Advances in the construction of accelerators eventually made it possible to give an affirmative answer to these questions, but these developments did not take place until 1955.

8

The Neutron, Artificial Radio-Activity, the Neutrino and Mesons

The work on cosmic radiation and the abnormal absorption of high-energy γ-particles, went hand in hand with research on the atomic nucleus which, since the time of Rutherford's experiments, was increasingly absorbing the energy of physicists. In 1930, all that was known about the nucleus was that it gave rise to natural radio-active rays, and that some of these rays were electrons. It was therefore thought that the atomic nucleus was made up of electrons as well as of protons. The helium nucleus, for example, was said to consist of 4 protons and 2 electrons, i.e. 6 elementary particles of spin $\frac{1}{2}$.

Wave mechanics could not account for the presence of these electrons in the atomic nucleus, since the dimensions of the electrons exceeded those of the nucleus.

The neutron. Rutherford's work was followed up by Bothe and Becker in Germany. By bombarding light elements (such as boron and beryllium) with α-rays emitted by polonium, they discovered a new type of nuclear transformation.

In this case, it was not a proton which was emitted from the nucleus, but some radiation of great penetrative power and of very weak intensity. Bothe and Becker concluded that this radiation was electro-magnetic.

Two years later, in 1932, the experiments were repeated by Chadwick in England, and by I. and F. Joliot-Curie in France. They found that this new radiation could knock out hydrogen nuclei in its path. Chadwick was therefore able to conclude that the radiation responsible for projecting the protons must have consisted of neutral particles with a mass close to that of the proton. These particles were called neutrons.

Because it has no charge, the neutron's passage through matter cannot be detected, unless it happens to lose some of its energy in collision with a nearby atomic nucleus. Such collisions are very rare, and the neutron can in fact pass through thick layers of matter.

By the end of 1932, neutrons had taken the place of electrons in the picture of the structure of the nucleus. The helium nucleus was now thought to consist of 4, instead of 6, particles—2 protons and 2 neutrons. A great many difficulties had been resolved, and the existence of isotopes could at last be explained.

Two isotopic nuclei are two nuclei with the same number of protons Z, but with a different number of neutrons A—Z (where A is the atomic weight). The electron shells in the two isotopes are identical since they are still made up of Z electrons revolving about the nucleus of positive charge Ze. As a result, the two isotopes have identical chemical properties. Since, however, the nuclei do not have the same number of neutrons, they may have different radio-active properties.

Chemical elements could now be represented by their chemical symbols with a subscript giving the charge Z and a superscript giving the total number of protons and neutrons in the nucleus. For instance, Cl_{17}^{35} and Cl_{17}^{37} are the 2 stable isotopes of chlorine.

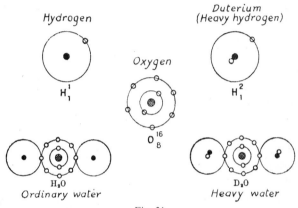

Fig. 31
Examples of isotopes.

Though the neutron helped to explain a great many phenomena, the interpretation of its emission and the determination of its exact mass presented new problems. Experimental work was therefore directed to a detailed study of the transmutations produced by α-particles.

In the course of this work, I. and F. Joliot-Curie observed that certain light elements—fluorine, aluminium and sodium—emitted positive and negative electrons when bombarded with α-rays from plutonium. Thus they had shown that a neutron and a positive electron (transmutation electron) could be emitted in place of a proton (whose mass is $1 \cdot 00795$).

Was the anti-electron a constituent of the atomic nucleus, just like the electron?

One of the first consequences of these experiments was the determination of the mass of the neutron. The Curies obtained the value

$$1 \cdot 00890 < M_n < 1 \cdot 0100.$$

The current value is $M_n = 1 \cdot 00898$. The mass of the neutron is therefore slightly greater than that of the proton.

The second consequence of these experiments was the discovery of artificial radio-activity, which was to earn the Joliot-Curies the Nobel Prize in 1935.

Artificial radio-activity. The emission of positive electrons by F, Al, Na continues even after the bombardment with α-particles has stopped. The emitted rays are of the same nature as the β-rays emitted by radio-active elements.

Bombardment with α-particles produces unstable elements not normally found in nature, which then disintegrate in the course of time to produce stable elements.

We can now write down the reactions set off by α-particles or He_2^4 nuclei. For instance, the bombardment of aluminium sets off the following reaction:

$$Al_{13}^{27} + He_2^4 \rightarrow P_{15}^{30} + n_0^1 \nearrow$$

The phosphorus thus formed is unstable:

$$P_{15}^{30} \rightarrow Si_{14}^{30} + e^+ \nearrow$$

Its radio-active half-life is of the order of a few minutes.

By 1932, matter was thus thought to have 3 elementary constituents: the electron, the proton, and the neutron, all of spin $\frac{1}{2}$, and hence in agreement with Dirac's theory. While theory was satisfied with this new picture of the nucleus, experiment was not. Physicists could not explain how β-rays, i.e. the electrons, could have left the nucleus of which they had not originally been a part.

Once again the theoreticians had to be called in. They put forward the idea that neutrons and protons were 2 different states of one and the same particle, the nucleon. The nucleon could undergo two transitions:

neutron → proton + negative electron
proton → neutron + positive electron

Resultant spin : 1

Resultant spin : 0

Proton

Electron

Spin 1/2

Fig. 32
Model of the neutron.

While the existence of artificial radio-activity could now be explained, there still remained one great theoretical difficulty: since a neutron with spin $\frac{1}{2}$ is made up of 2 particles each of spin $\frac{1}{2}$, the resultant spin could only be either 0 or 1, and not $\frac{1}{2}$, as in fact it was (see Fig. 32).

There was another, experimental, difficulty. The principle of the conservation of energy is not observed in the course of β-decay. The electron emitted by the nucleus does not carry all the lost energy. For instance, when a nucleus of radio-phosphorus P^{32}_{15} (an unstable isotope of P^{31}_{15}) disintegrates, the resulting nucleus is a nucleus of stable sulphur S^{32}_{16}. The difference of energy between P^{32}_{15} and S^{32}_{16} is about 1·7 MeV, which ought to be the energy of the decay electron. Now this is not the case—the electrons emitted by radio-phosphorus have a continuous energy distribution ranging between 0 and 1·7 MeV.

The neutrino. Since previous hypotheses of the existence of new particles had proved so fruitful, physicists, in order to account for the above results, postulated the existence of a particle of charge zero and of much smaller mass than the electron: the neutrino.

Experimental workers, with considerable technological efforts and using a great deal of ingenuity, have actually managed to demonstrate the existence of this new, neutral, particle. This work continues, and scientists are at present investigating if—in accordance with Dirac's theory—an anti-neutrino exists by the side of the neutrino.

We must now distinguish between the essential characteristics of elementary particles and their anti-particles.

According to Dirac's theory, both particles and anti-particles have a positive kinetic energy, and can therefore not be distinguished by their mass. There

are, however, two other distinguishing characteristics: charge and magnetic moment.

In the case of a charged particle (proton or electron) the problem is simple: charge and spin turn
the particle into a small magnet with a characteristic
magnetic moment; the anti-particle will then be of
opposite charge and have a magnetic moment in the
opposite sense to that of the particle.

The proton has the charge $+ e$, and the magnetic
moment:

$$\mu_p = 2 \cdot 79 \frac{eh}{4 \pi M_p c}$$

and the anti-proton the charge $- e$ and the magnetic
moment:

$$- 2 \cdot 79 \frac{eh}{4 \pi M_p c}.$$

The problem is more difficult for the case of neutral
particles, since it is difficult to see how a particle
without charge can have a magnetic moment. This
being the case, it seems impossible to distinguish
between neutral anti-particles and neutral particles.

But, in fact, a particle could be electrically neutral
and still carry positive and negative charges cancel-
ling each other. A magnetic moment could then
result from the motion of these charges, and particles
could therefore be distinguished from anti-particles
by the sign of their magnetic moments.

By experiment, the magnetic moment of the
neutron was shown to be:

$$\mu_n = - 1 \cdot 91 \frac{eh}{4 \pi M_p c}.$$

The magnetic moment, which has a direction parallel to the spin, has in the case of the neutron, a sense opposite to the spin.

The neutrino has the magnetic moment $\mu \simeq 0$. If $\mu = 0$, the anti-neutrino and the neutrino are identical, but if $\mu \neq 0$ they could be distinguished. The mass of the neutrino is very small compared to that of an electron (m_0), and may be as small as $10^{-6} m_0$.

All these factors make the neutrino very difficult to detect. However, the introduction of a particle of spin $\frac{1}{2}$ into the theory of β-decay means that the laws of the conservation of spin and energy are obeyed.

$$n \rightarrow p + e^- + \bar{\nu}$$
$$p \rightarrow n + e^+ + \nu$$

The presence of the anti-neutrino (ν) lends greater symmetry to the theory of β radiation:

$$n + \nu \rightarrow p + e^-$$
$$p + \bar{\nu} \rightarrow n + e^+$$

The emission of a neutrino thus corresponds to the absorption of an anti-neutrino, and vice versa. In this way, a β-transition transforming the nucleus (A, Z) into the nucleus (A, Z + 1), can be explained as the absorption by a neutron of the original nucleus of a neutrino with its consequent transformation into a proton and emission of a negative electron. Considered in this way, the neutrons and protons in the nucleus can absorb and emit light particles (electron-neutrino) and are thus mutually transformable.

This touches upon a question which was claiming

the attention of theoreticians in 1935. How can we explain the cohesion between protons and neutrons within the confined nuclear space where the electrostatic repulsion between, for instance, 2 protons must be considerable? Since Coulombian forces could not explain their cohesion, bonds of an entirely new nature had to be introduced. Physicists looked at the example of the hydrogen molecule.

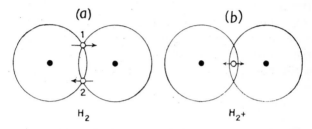

Fig. 33
Hydrogen molecule. (a) Neutral, and (b) Ionised.

Now, in the hydrogen molecule, H_2 (Fig. 33), the spins of the 2 electrons are anti-parallel. The system is stable, and wave mechanics could, in fact, predict this stability from the wave functions ψ_1 and ψ_2 of the 2 electrons.

Once an electron is torn from this molecule, the molecule becomes a positive ion, and a single electron must preserve the stability of the system. The electron is then said to oscillate between the 2 protons, thus holding them together despite their electrostatic repulsion.

By analogy, this kind of exchange was thought to be responsible for the cohesion of nucleons within a nucleus, and the neutrino and the electron were thought to be the particles involved in the exchange. The nuclear radius predicted by this hypothesis was much larger than the experimentally measured radius; and hence an entirely new particle, the meson, was postulated.

Since then, mesons have assumed an ever-growing importance in atomic physics, and must certainly be considered as playing a paramount role within the nucleus. We shall therefore have to look at them more closely.

Mesons. In 1935, the Japanese physicist Yukawa suggested that an exchange of mesons took place between the nucleons of the nucleus and that it was responsible for the stability of atomic nuclei. He predicted that the mesons would have a mass 200 times that of the electron, and that their lifetime was of the order of a millionth of a second (10^{-6} sec.).

In May 1937, experiments confirmed the existence of this hypothetical particle. The study of cosmic rays, which had already confirmed the existence of Dirac's positive electron, now revealed the existence of Yukawa's meson. The mass of the first meson to be identified was roughly 210 times the mass of the electron ($210 \ m_e$)—theory had once again been corroborated. Cloud-chamber photographs, furthermore, showed that a meson could disintegrate with the appearance of an electron. This type of meson, called a μ-meson, exists in two states μ^+ and μ^-, of charges $+ \ e$ and $- \ e$ and of spin $\frac{1}{2}$. Hence the symmetry between particle and anti-particle held good in this field as well.

The energy of the electrons emitted during the disintegration of a μ-meson is not always the same.

This was thought to result from the fact that the μ-meson breaks up into three particles:

$$\mu^+ \to e^+ + \nu + \overline{\nu}$$
$$\mu^- \to e^- + \nu + \overline{\nu}$$

The mean life of a μ-meson is $2 \cdot 15.10^{-6}$ sec. The meson itself results from the disintegration of another type of meson (π-meson) which, though discovered later than the μ-meson, must be considered to be the original Yukawa particle.

The π meson, of mass 275 m_e exists in 3 states: π^+, π^-, and π^0 (neutral meson). Perfect symmetry holds between π^+ and π^-, both of which have a mean life of $2 \cdot 5.10^{-8}$ sec. π^0 has a somewhat smaller mass (265 m_e) and a very much smaller half-life (10^{-15} sec.). It appears that π mesons have spin 0, which differentiates them from the class of particles obeying Dirac's equation.

It is the π-mesons which are responsible for the cohesive forces within the nucleus; according to the following scheme:

1) $P \rightleftharpoons N + \pi^+$ 2) $N \rightleftharpoons P + \pi^-$
3) $P \rightleftharpoons P + \pi^0$ 4) $N \rightleftharpoons P + \pi^0$

When the work on mesons was first begun, cosmic radiation was the sole known source of these new particles. They were generally studied by means of the Wilson cloud-chamber. However, Yukawa's theory had predicted that mesons could arise from collisions between two high velocity nucleons, in the following scheme:

$$N_1 + N_2 \to N_1' + N_2' + \pi$$

Developments in accelerator techniques and in methods of observation were to confirm this theory and to provide new sources of mesons together with new methods of studying them.

Heavy mesons or hyperons were discovered, and in due course these particles were to provide the energy needed for the creation of anti-nucleons.

9

Particle Accelerators
and High-Energy Physics

As far back as 1933, the Solvay Congress had already discussed 'the disintegration of elements by accelerated protons'. J. D. Cockcroft pointed out that, according to wave mechanics, very high energies were not really essential for penetrating the nucleus, and added that the success of artificial nuclear disintegration generally depended on the production of a current of fast-moving particles. Different methods had been used for this purpose but considerable technical difficulties had been met in all of them.

Thus, from the time that Dirac had mooted the idea of antiparticles, physicists had been looking for ways and means of accelerating the then known particles in order to produce projectiles for splitting the nucleus.

Cockcroft and Walton, by accelerating protons in an electrostatic field of some hundred thousand volts, had, in fact, managed to split the lithium nucleus into two α-particles:

$$\mathrm{Li}_3^7 + \mathrm{H}_1^1 \rightarrow 2 \ \mathrm{He}_2^4$$

A new branch of physics was therefore born at the 1933 Congress, when Cockcroft and Walton presented their results in the presence of Rutherford, the father of nuclear transformations, and Lawrence, the builder of the first cyclotron.

Lawrence's cyclotron at Berkeley, California, was the first of a series of powerful accelerators. With them, physics was to make tremendous strides, and open up the field of nuclear reactions in the same revolutionary way that 19th century chemists had opened up the field of chemical reactions. This progress is continuing to this day, and modern technical knowledge is being applied to the construction of ever-more powerful accelerators.

Since particle-accelerators made possible the production of mesons in 1947, of anti-protons in 1955, and of anti-neutrons in 1956, we shall now give a brief sketch of the most important of them.

General Principles. Whenever a charged particle is placed in an electric field, it becomes accelerated. Charged particles (ions) are produced in the following ways:

Protons, by the ionisation of hydrogen.

Deuterons, by the ionisation of heavy hydrogen.

α-particles, by the ionisation of helium.

All accelerators have, first of all, a source of ions—i.e., a chamber in which the gas (hydrogen or helium) is reduced to very low pressures (10^{-3} to 10^{-4} cm. of mercury) and in which it is ionised. The resulting ions are then forced into the accelerator proper, where the pressure is much lower still (10^{-6} to 10^{-7} cm. of mercury). Finally, the accelerated particles are expelled to give a beam whose intensity can be calculated with a high degree of accuracy.

The Electrostatic Accelerator. Van de Graaf's

electrostatic accelerator produces a beam of particles (protons or deuterons) of continuous intensity and of a definite amount of energy, which can be calculated within an error of 1/10,000.

This type of linear accelerator is based on a very simple principle. When a particle of charge Ze travels between two electrodes whose potential difference is V volts, it is given the energy ZeV electron-volts. Cockcroft and Walton's accelerator in the Cavendish Laboratory at Cambridge was based on this idea. Here, protons were accelerated by applying potentials of about 100 kV to a set of successive electrodes.

In the Van de Graaf accelerator, an endless belt of insulating material is sprayed with positive ions from a D.C. generator. The charge is collected by a hollow sphere acting as an electrode.

Thus a high potential difference, V, is set up between the electrode and the earth, and this potential is limited only by the nature of the insulating material, and by the dimensions of the apparatus.

The Cyclotron. In Lawrence's cyclotron the ions are accelerated by the application of numerous successive potentials.

The ions move in a circular orbit due to the lateral force of a magnetic field. Acceleration is effected between two flat, semi-circular containers, the 'dees' (i.e., D-shapes), to which a high frequency A.C. potential is applied. The dees are placed in a strong magnetic field and, at each half-period, the ions are pulled into one of the containers. The frequency of the applied alternating field is chosen so that the particles, after describing one semi-circle, enter into the opposite field between the dees, and are thus accelerated further. This process is repeated a few hundred times, so that very fast-moving ions are produced, although the voltages involved are relatively small.

The cyclotron produces a beam of particles (protons, deuterons and α-particles) of very great kinetic energy (in the case of deuterons up to 25 MeV).

In a magnetic field $\vec{H}$, perpendicular to $\vec{v}$, a particle of mass M, of charge $q = Ze$, and of velocity $\vec{v}$ describes a circular trajectory of radius ρ.

The radius is calculated by putting that, on this trajectory, the Lorentz and centrifugal forces are in equilibrium.

$$F_L = \frac{qvH}{c}; \; F_c = \frac{Mv^2}{\rho} \; \text{whence} \; \frac{Mv}{\rho} = \frac{qH}{c} \text{and} \frac{\rho}{v} = \frac{Mc}{qH}$$

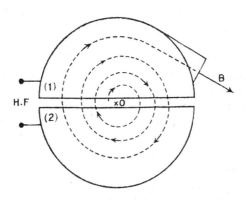

Fig. 34

The cyclotron. O, source of ions. (1) and (2), dees. B, beam of accelerated particles. H.F., high frequency. The magnetic field is perpendicular to the plane of the figure.

The period of rotation t of the charged particles in the magnetic field is $2\pi\rho/v = 2\pi\dfrac{Mc}{qH}$, i.e. the period is independent of the velocity provided only that v is small compared with c, i.e. provided relativity effects can be neglected. The duration of one revolution can therefore be so adjusted as to be equal to the period of the high frequency potential.

Putting $\dfrac{v}{\rho} = \omega$, we then obtain:

$$Mc^2 = \frac{qHc^2}{\omega} = \frac{qHc}{v/c}$$

where M is the relativistic mass

$$M = M_0 \Big/ \sqrt{1 - \frac{v^2}{c^2}} = M_0\gamma.$$

We know that Mc^2 is the total energy of the particle

$$Mc^2 = W_{kin} + M_0c^2$$

where W_{kin} is the kinetic energy of the particle, and M_0c^2 the equivalent energy of the inertial mass.

The maximum kinetic energy for a given particle depends on the radius of the orbit in the magnetic field, and on either the frequency of the oscillator, or the intensity of the field.

Lawrence's first cyclotron had the following characteristics:

Diameter of the electrodes: 50 cm;
Diameter of the electromagnet: 114 cm;
Deuteron beam of $3 \cdot 6$ MeV.

The magnetic field H of the cyclotron is usually between 5,000 and 15,000 gauss. Once H is fixed, the energy of the particle depends on its charge and on the radius ρ of its maximum orbit. With $H = 10,000$ gauss and $\rho = 50$ cm, deuterons of 6 MeV and protons of 12 MeV are produced. With $H = 13,000$ gauss and $\rho = 250$ cm, the particles will have the respective energies of 238 MeV and 415 MeV. With such energies the velocity would approach that of light, and the period of rotation would no longer be independent of the velocity. Thus an upper limit is set to the possible particle energies produced in cyclotrons.

The Synchro-cyclotron. The orbital radius of an accelerated particle in the cyclotron is given by

$$\rho = \frac{M_0 v \gamma}{qH}; \; \gamma = 1 \Big/ \sqrt{1 - \frac{v^2}{c^2}}$$

and the time of one revolution by

$$t = \frac{2\pi\rho}{v} = \frac{2\pi M_0 \gamma}{qH}.$$

When v is small compared with c (the velocity of light) we have $\gamma = 1 \Big/ \sqrt{1 - \frac{v^2}{c^2}} = 1$ and, by putting $t = $ const. we can obtain a constant frequency f, such that

$$f = \frac{qH}{2\pi M_0 \gamma}.$$

Once the velocity of light is approached, the parameter γ becomes a function of the velocity of the particle, i.e. of the radius ρ of the trajectory; $\gamma(\rho)$ becomes greater than unity and, since t is no longer constant, a phase lag occurs between the arrival of the particle in the dees and the time of maximum voltage.

When this lag corresponds to 90°, the voltage is zero and the particle is not accelerated between the dees; it moves in an orbit of fixed radius.

In the synchro-cyclotron, this decrease in angular velocity is compensated by a corresponding decrease in the frequency applied to the dees. This frequency modulation may lead to very high energies and produce a beam of particles whose intensity is no longer constant. The resulting pulses are in the micro-ampère range.

The Berkeley synchro-cyclotron, completed in 1946, gives a beam of deuterons of 200 MeV, and of α-particles of 400 MeV. To construct this gigantic apparatus, 3,500 tons of steel were needed.

The Betatron. The betatron does not have a high frequency electric field. A variable magnetic field H sets up an electrical field E which, in turn, induces a magnetic field H'. The field H' tends to oppose the variations of H. The acceleration is produced in a circular chamber between the poles of an annular electro-magnet. The poles are constructed so as to assure a stable trajectory for the particle.

The betatron is particularly suitable for accelerating electrons. These are introduced with an energy of 60 KeV and accelerated in a chosen orbit by the induced electric field. When they hit a target, high energy γ-radiation is produced which can be used for splitting nuclei (photo-nuclear reactions).

The energy obtained in the betatron is set an upper limit by the radius of the trajectory and by the maximum intensity of the magnetic field.

The betatron provides electrons of 25 MeV, its weight is 5 tons, the orbital radius is 20 cm, and the magnetic field at the orbit is 4,000 gauss.

The Synchrotron. The synchrotron has an annular electromagnet like the Betatron, and an accelerator which, like that of the cyclotron, consists of a number N of accelerating electrodes to which an A.C. field is applied. The accelerated particles are kept on a stable orbit with mean radius $\bar{\rho}$ by means of changes in the field H and by modulating the frequency of the alternating potential. The particles bunch into a packet which receives N accelerating impulses per turn.

In the synchrotron, the ions must first be passed through an electrostatic device to give them just the right energy needed for introducing them into their orbit by the accelerator circuit.

In the electron-synchrotron, the electrons are first accelerated by a betatron to a velocity close to that of light. They are then introduced into the synchrotron at an energy of 2MeV.

The synchrotron at Cornell University weighs 738 tons, the radius of the orbit is about one metre, and the electrons have an energy of 300 MeV when they strike the target.

In the proton-synchrotron the preliminary accelerator is of the Van de Graaf type. From it, the protons are introduced into the synchrotron proper with an energy of between 3 and 10 MeV.

The main characteristics of such an accelerator are quite astounding:

1650 tons of steel,

70 tons of copper,

Maximum current in the magnetic lenses: 7,000 A,
Orbital radius: 10 metres,
Energy of protons on leaving the synchrotron:
    3,000 million electron volts.

These figures (cosmotron of Brookhaven) have
been exceeded by the bevatron of Berkeley, which
provides protons with an energy of 6,200 million
electron volts.

These accelerators are a long way from the original
models presented by Cockcroft and Lawrence in
1933. Even so, the possibilities of the less powerful
accelerators are by no means exhausted.

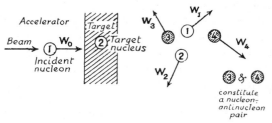

Fig. 35
Creation of anti-nucleons through the collision of two nucleons.

The inertial mass of the electron represents an
energy of $0 \cdot 510$ MeV. An energy of $1 \cdot 02$ MeV is
therefore needed for creating an e^+, e^- pair. This
energy was found in cosmic radiation and in the
radiation of certain radio-active elements. Anti-
electrons could therefore be observed in the laboratory without all this tremendous effort.

The creation of a pair of mesons, with a mass 200
times that of the electron, requires an energy of 200
MeV. Though this energy could not have been
achieved with the smaller accelerators, processes

involving this energy are present in cosmic radiation, in which mesons were in fact first observed. On the other hand, since the mass of the proton is 1,840 times that of the electron, 938 MeV is needed to create it, and 1,876 MeV for creating a pair of nucleons.

In the Berkeley experiment, this amount of energy was, in fact, supplied by the collision of two nucleons. If the incident nucleon has the kinetic energy W_0 before the collision it will have the kinetic energy W_1 after the collision, while the target nucleus will be deflected with kinetic energy W_2. The two newly created nucleons will have the energies W_3 and W_4 and an energy of approximately 2,000 MeV will have gone into their creation.

By the law of the conservation of energy, we can represent conditions before and after the collision:

$$W_0 = 2{,}000 \text{ M}e\text{V} + W_1 + W_2 + W_3 + W_4.$$

The equation shows that roughly $W_0 = 6{,}000$ MeV is needed for the creation of a pair of nucleons. With this enormous amount of energy, new antiparticles could be created, the validity of the theory could be tested and new phenomena might be observed.

These great energies, these gigantic machines, these towers of concrete and steel, this fantastic expenditure, this mobilisation of manpower and resources were therefore needed if physicists were to test the validity of Dirac's suggestion that there were negative energy levels for protons, which were normally occupied, but which when unoccupied would appear as anti-protons.

10

Production of Anti-Nucleons

While the construction of giant accelerators was proceeding apace, cosmic ray specialists were concentrating on the development of new photographic plate techniques.

In 1947, scientists had observed that an enormous amount of energy was liberated whenever an ionising cosmic particle passing through a photographic emulsion was stopped in its path. By 1954, the study of the energy processes represented by some of these photographic tracks had led scientists to suspect that the tracks were due to the annihilation of anti-protons or anti-hyperons.

Like anti-electrons, anti-protons were probably first observed in cosmic radiation, later to be re-created in the laboratory.

The reader will remember that, during 1930-1932, scientists were busily repeating Rutherford's experiments on the absorption of high-velocity γ-radiation. At that time, 'high energy' referred to energies greater than one million electron-volts. Nowadays this figure has become outdated, and when we speak of high energy today, we mean energies greater than 1,000 million electron-volts.

The reader will therefore not be surprised to learn

of the corresponding advances in technique. Many laboratories have, in fact, been turned into veritable factories employing a vast number of specialists.

The electroscope, the Wilson cloud-chamber, and the Geiger counter are things of the past; in their stead new detection-techniques have been developed. We shall now examine these very briefly.

1. *Plate techniques.* A photographic emulsion consisting of micro-crystals of silver bromide (AgBr) in gelatine is deposited on a glass plate.

When an ionised particle passes through the emulsion, it loses some of its energy, with the result that the silver bromide crystals along its path turn into grains of silver which are detectable when the emulsion is developed. If these grains are sufficiently close to one another (which depends on the amount of energy dissipated per unit length of path), they form a track representing the path of the particle through the emulsion. From the length of the track the energy of the particle can be calculated, and from the distribution of the silver grains along the track, its mass can be evaluated.

Plate techniques have been greatly improved within the last two years, particularly for the study of cosmic rays and mesons.

2. *The Scintillation counter.* The scintillation counter is generally made up of a sodium iodide crystal (or another transparent substance) in which the absorption of a particle or of γ-radiation produces ionisation phenomena, and a photo-multiplier which transforms the light emitted by the crystal into a measurable electric current.

When an ionising particle hits an atom inside

the crystal, it disturbs the electronic structure of that atom. Its return to the stable state is accompanied by the emission of light, i.e. by a series of scintillations along the path of the particle in the crystal. This light, the intensity of which is proportional to the energy lost by the ionising particle through absorption, is directed at the sensitised layer of a photo-multiplier from which it ejects electrons (photo-electric effect). These electrons are in turn accelerated by the constant potential and multiplied by the action of special electrodes (dynodes) of ever-increasing potential.

By means of the photo-multiplier, the electric charge has been magnified by a factor of 10^6 to 10^9, and can therefore be detected. It is proportional to the energy of the particles absorbed in the crystal. Thus, unlike the Geiger-Müller counter, the scintillation counter not only detects the ionisation phenomena, but also measures the energies involved.

3. *Cerenkov counters.* When a particle of great velocity passes through a solid transparent medium, it may, under certain circumstances, emit electromagnetic radiation known as Cerenkov radiation. For this to happen, the velocity of light in the solid medium must be lower than the velocity of the particle.

If n is the refractive index of the transparent medium, and c is the velocity of light *in vacuo*, the velocity of light in the solid medium is: $u = c/n$. The condition for the emission of Cerenkov radiation is $v > u$, where v is the velocity of the particle.

The Cerenkov effect can be compared to a shock wave produced by a bullet travelling with supersonic velocity. A disturbance then takes place within a cone whose apex is formed by the bullet. The vertical angle θ is defined by

$$\cos \theta = \frac{u}{v}$$

The angle θ is therefore a measure of the kinetic energy of the bullet or, in our case, the particle.

Cerenkov radiation can be used for detecting high energy particles such as protons with kinetic energies greater than 300 MeV.

Let us now return to Berkeley, with its giant synchro-cyclotron capable of producing α-particles of 380 MeV. At the beginning of 1948, mesons were detected on photographic plates placed near the carbon target of this instrument. Their trajectory ended in a 'star', representing the break-up of a nucleus with which the meson had collided.

Theory had once again been borne out by experiment, and since then, π-mesons have been produced by the use of γ-rays of 335 MeV obtained from the synchrotron. In this reaction a neutron is transformed into a proton:

$$\gamma + N \rightarrow P + \pi^-.$$

Transmutation on the nuclear scale (1920) had thus given way to transformations of the very particles of which the nucleus is made up.

In 1955, scientists at Berkeley were ready to tackle the creation of the anti-proton.

The anti-proton. Theoretically, two different methods could be used for the creation of the proton-anti-proton pair.

1. The collision of a proton p with a nucleon N

$$p + N \rightarrow p + N' + p + \bar{p}$$

In this type of reaction, the incident proton must have the kinetic energy 5,600 MeV.

2. The creation is effected in two stages; the preliminary creation of an high energy π-meson leads to the creation of an anti-proton after collision with an N nucleon:

$$\pi + N \rightarrow N' + p + \bar{p}.$$

This process, though more complicated, requires incident protons of smaller energy (4,100 MeV). (The Berkeley bevatron could produce a beam of protons of 6,200 MeV).

The production of a new particle is one thing. Its detection, i.e. the demonstration of its characteristic properties, is another. The main problem was, indeed, to perfect identification techniques, the exact details of which fall outside the scope of this book. The general principles employed are, however, as follows.

As it left the bevatron, the proton beam was intercepted by a copper screen. This screen, which provided the nucleons, gave off a host of charged and neutral particles amongst which the anti-protons had now to be identified.

Deflection by the magnetic field of the bevatron made possible the preliminary selection of negative particles only. Apart from anti-protons, these consisted of a large quantity of π^--mesons.

Anti-protons had therefore to be distinguished from the mesons by their respective masses.

Every particle (π^- and p^-) can be characterised by its kinetic energy $\frac{1}{2} mv^2$ and by its momentum $\vec{p} = m\vec{v}$. Once $\vec{p}$ and $\vec{v}$ are known, the mass of the particle can be calculated.

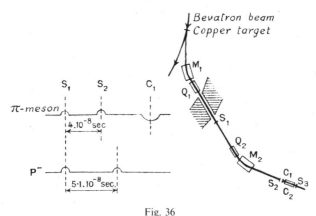

Fig. 36

Experimental arrangement used with bevatron (Berkeley, Calif.). Impulses registered by the counters S_1, S_2 and C_1.

A system of magnetic and electric lenses M_1, Q_1, Q_2, M_2, can be used for focussing negative particles with the same momentum on a scintillation counter S_2 with an accuracy of 2 per cent (Fig. 36). From the knowledge of the masses it was known that the value of p chosen corresponded to a velocity $v_p = 0\cdot78\ c$ for a proton and to a velocity $v_\pi = 0\cdot99$ c for a meson. To separate anti-protons from the π^--mesons the particles were passed through another scintillation counter S_1, placed 12 metres along their path in front of S_2.

While π^--mesons took 4.10^{-8} sec. to clear the distance between the two scintillators S_1 and S_2, anti-protons of the same momentum took $5 \cdot 1.10^{-8}$ sec. The coincidence circuit connecting S_1 and S_2 was thus adjusted to count only impulses separated by $5 \cdot 1.10^{-8}$ sec., i.e. to eliminate the π^--mesons.

To make doubly sure, the negative particles—all of the same momentum—were further passed through two Cerenkov counters C_1 and C_2 and a third scintillator S_3. The counter C_1 is sensitive to all charged particles with a velocity greater than $0 \cdot 79$ c, while the counter C_2 is sensitive to particles with a velocity ranging between

$$0 \cdot 75 \, c < v < 0 \cdot 78 \, c$$

Clearly, while C_1 records the passage of π^--mesons, C_2 registers the passage of anti-protons.

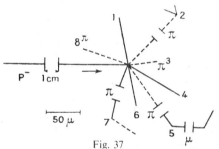

Fig. 37

Star arising from the annihilation of an anti-proton. The lines 1, 4 and 6 correspond to heavy particles, the others to π-mesons.

By establishing a further coincidence circuit between S_1, S_2 and C_2, two independent determinations of the velocity could be made. A third scintillator S_3 was placed behind S_1, S_2 and C_2, to make perfectly certain that the detected particle had crossed C_2 along its axis.

On the 24th October 1955, the physicists of Berkeley could claim that they had detected sixty anti-protons to date.

Anti-protons were also detected on photographic plates. Their annihilation was marked by an eight-branched star representing heavy particles—probably protons—and light particles, π-mesons (Fig. 37).

In March 1956, a plate exposed to a proton beam from the bevatron, showed a line connecting two high-energy stars. This line was identified as belonging to an anti-proton of kinetic energy 710 MeV. A calculation of the energy represented by the second star showed that the liberated energy must have exceeded 1,460 MeV.

While the first star was due to the collision between a proton and a heavy nucleus with the consequent creation of an anti-proton, the second star represented the annihilation of that anti-proton.

The annihilation of the anti-proton is corroborative evidence for its creation.

For the last few years, theoreticians have been wondering what would happen when an anti-nucleon collides with a corresponding nucleon. Like the e^+, e^- pair, the two nucleons ought to annihilate each other with the consequent liberation of energy. In the case of the p^+, p^- pair, this energy is 2 M$_p$$c^2$. It was thought that while this annihilation might be accompanied by the creation of two photons (as frequently happens in the case of electron collisions), the more probable process was the emission of two π-mesons of equal and opposite momentum.

Fermi even asserted that the available energy was great enough to produce more than two mesons and that other processes (the emission of heavy particles) were even more probable.

It was this, which had, in fact, been observed on photographic plates at Berkeley.

The anti-neutron. Neutrons, as we have seen, are exceedingly difficult to detect. Their lack of charge, and the consequent absence of ionising effects mean that neutrons leave no trace on photographic plates and pass through scintillation counters with little chance of detection. On the other hand, when an anti-neutron is destroyed, it liberates the energy $M_n c^2$ and can then be detected.

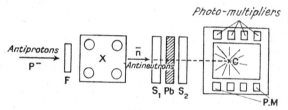

Fig. 38

Experimental arrangement to demonstrate the existence of anti-neutrons. The anti-neutrons pass through the scintillation counters S_1 and S_2 without being detected. When they are annihilated in the Cerenkov counter C, the photo-multipliers record the light emitted. This is proportional to the energy liberated. F, counter recording 300 to 600 antiprotons per hour. X, anti-proton-anti-neutron converter. Pb, lead screen for converting high energy γ-radiation into electrons.

Anti-neutrons were produced from anti-protons when, during a collision, they exchanged charges (Fig. 38). Even so, the effect was weak and a very strong beam of protons was required to demonstrate it.

300-600 anti-protons per hour were fed into an anti-proton anti-neutron 'convertor'. The newly created anti-neutrons were then passed undetected through the scintillators S_1 and S_2 finally to be annihilated in a Cerenkov counter. The magnitude of the resulting impulse gives a measure of the energy liberated by the annihilation of a nucleon-anti-nucleon pair.

Other neutral radiation is also emitted from the convertor, namely neutral mesons heavier than π_0 mesons and γ-radiation. Neutral mesons produce weak impulses in the Cerenkov counter, and γ-radiation is converted into electrons by a lead screen placed between the scintillators S_1 and S_2.

The distribution of impulses produced by the anti-neutrons was compared with the energy spectrum of the anti-protons. The spectra were found to be comparable, and the existence of anti-neutrons was thus established.

Since then, the new anti-particles have been the object of the most careful studies, though these are necessarily difficult because of the weak intensities available. Even so, scientists have been able to compare the absorption of anti-protons and protons by beryllium and copper. The absorption of anti-protons was found to be about twice that of protons.

Does this mean that the anti-proton has a greater radius than the proton, or that nuclei behave differently in the vicinity of anti-protons? While it is too early to say, the first assumption must be rejected out of hand, since the factor 2 does not apply equally to copper and to beryllium.

Similar and other questions can be asked about the anti-neutron. Is the anti-neutron, like the neutron, an unstable particle, and does it disintegrate to give an anti-proton, a positive electron and an anti-neutrino? The answer lies in the hands of the experimental physicists.

11

Matter and Antimatter

We have seen how the study of electric discharges in cathode-ray tubes led to the detection of the electron, and how Rutherford's work brought in its wake the exploration of the nucleus with the subsequent discovery of its constituents, the proton and the neutron. The study of β-decay led to the discovery of the neutrino, and that of nuclear stability to the discovery of mesons.

We can now construct an entirely new model of the atom.

At the centre, it has a nucleus in which protons and neutrons are held together by the exchange of π^0, π^+ and π^- mesons. This nucleus is surrounded by electrons, which often revolve at considerable distances from it and envelop the central positive charge with an atmosphere of negative electricity.

We know that this model is based both on classical physics and on wave mechanics. The Bohr-Sommerfeld atom helps us to bridge the gap between abstract verbal concepts of discontinuity and their mathematical expression.

Once we adopt this picture of matter, we are forced to look into the problem of antimatter also.

Now, the idea of antimatter arose as a direct result of mathematical considerations which had come to replace what were felt to be inadequate visual representations of the atom. These mathematical considerations were:

1. Relativity theory, which introduced a new expression for the energy of the particle

$$(E = \pm c\sqrt{p^2 + m_0c^2}).$$

2. Quantum theory, which led to the consideration of negative energies.

3. Relativistic wave mechanics, which gave a correct representation of the properties of the electron.

We have seen how the theory of holes, by giving a definite meaning to electrons of negative energy, was able to predict the existence of new particles and to give a precise definition of their properties. Particle and anti-particle only differ in the signs of their charge and of their magnetic moment.

Theoretically predicted in 1930, anti-particles were soon to be demonstrated experimentally. The first to be detected was the anti-electron, or positive electron. Further progress had to await the construction of giant accelerators, when π^- and π^+ mesons could be produced in the synchro-cyclotron, and anti-protons and anti-neutrons in the bevatron.

More recently still, atomic piles have been used to prove the existence of the neutrino and the anti-neutrino, and by the end of 1956, all the anti-particles necessary for building a model of anti-matter had been observed. The present-day picture is, then, as follows:

The central anti-nucleus is made up of anti-protons and anti-neutrons, held together by the exchange of π^0, π^- and π^+ mesons. The anti-nucleus is surrounded by enti-electrons which often revolve at considerable distances from it and envelop the central negative charge with an atmosphere of positive electricity.

Does this picture of the anti-atom represent a physical reality? In other words, does anti-matter exist? One way to find out this would be to create it out of anti-protons and anti-electrons, but unfortunately this is a very difficult task. Though the dematerialisation of matter has long been achieved, its creation demands temperatures beyond our normal reach.

A helium nucleus, for instance, cannot simply be created from two protons and two neutrons, or from four protons and two negative electrons. These particles must undergo fusion, a reaction involving temperatures of the order found at the interior of the sun, i.e. some millions of degrees.

The formation of a helium nucleus from four protons takes place in accordance with the following reactions (carbon cycle):

$$\boxed{H_1^1} + C_6^{12} \rightarrow N_7^{13} + \gamma$$
$$N_7^{13} \rightarrow C_6^{13} + \boxed{e^+}$$
$$\boxed{H_1^1} + C_6^{13} \rightarrow N_7^{14} + \gamma$$
$$\boxed{H_1^1} + N_7^{14} \rightarrow O_8^{15} + \gamma$$
$$O_8^{15} \rightarrow N_7^{15} + \boxed{e^+}$$
$$\boxed{H_1^1} + N_7^{15} \rightarrow C_6^{12} + \boxed{He_2^4}$$

This series of reactions, in which C_6^{12} clearly plays the role of catalyst, liberates a tremendous amount of energy. The energy is due to a mass defect in the newly formed nucleus. Taking the atomic weight of oxygen as 16, the mass of the proton is $1 \cdot 007596$ and that of the neutron $1 \cdot 00898$. The four nucleons together have therefore a mass of $4 \cdot 033152$. Now the mass of the helium nucleus happens to be $4 \cdot 00280$. The mass defect of $0 \cdot 030352$ is due to the fusion which, as we have seen, involves a temperature of some millions of degrees.

Now, such temperatures do in fact exist in the stars where such reactions may easily take place. On earth, atomic explosions can give such high temperatures and cause the fusion of nucleons, and this is the reaction employed in the hydrogen bomb. Scientists have also succeeded in producing fusion temperatures in the laboratory, but on a much smaller scale, in such instruments as Zeta (1958). In the future, the energy derived from nuclear fusion may well compete with the energy derived from nuclear fission in atomic piles.

We have seen how matter can be created from its constituent elements. Is antimatter to be constructed in the same way? If we could fuse an antiproton into a positive electron, we might well have created the simplest anti-atom (anti-hydrogen), but what would we do with it once we had it?

Our laboratories, and the world in which we experiment, are made of matter, and anti-particles are characterised by the fact that they become annihilated in contact with their sister particles.

How could we prevent the positive hydrogen electron from meeting one of the negative electrons of which all matter is constituted? How could we preserve anti-hydrogen so that we might use it for synthesising anti-helium? How, in short, could we do experiments with antimatter at all?

Antimatter probably has a structure identical with that of matter, and it is not unreasonable to assume that some stars and even galaxies are made up of it. But we also know that the coexistence of the two types of matter is, in the present state of our knowledge, an unreasonable hypothesis, and that antimatter cannot be produced experimentally at present. We may, however, talk about it theoretically or mathematically.

We have seen that, in Relativity theory, the element *ds*, which represents the trajectory of the electron in space-time is given by

$$ds = \pm \sqrt{d^2dt^2 - d\sigma^2}$$

Now, if $+ds$ represents negative electrons with positive kinetic energy, which move from the past to the future, $-ds$ represents negative electrons with negative kinetic energy, which run a course opposite to that of ordinary time. In other words, the positive electron is a negative electron retracing the path of time.

Our reason may well boggle at this. In any case, a vast new horizon has opened before us, though physicists are not yet ready to probe all its depths and secrets; work on anti-particles is in its infancy. This work may one day throw new light on the problem of the structure of the elementary particles, a structure which today hides behind the abstract formalism of the wave function.

Will physics now return to the making of models, and seek for the internal structure of the elementary particle? Will the electron, like the atom, be split to yield its inner secrets?

It is one of physic's greatest attractions, J. J. Thomson said, that it lacks fixed limits, each discovery, far from being an end in itself, being but a pathway to unexplored territory. As long as science exists, there will always be a host of unresolved problems, and no physicist need worry about being kept idle.

INDEX

125